Principles of
LONDON UNDERGROUND OPERATIONS

Principles of
LONDON UNDERGROUND OPERATIONS

JOHN GLOVER

Ian Allan
PUBLISHING

First published 2000

ISBN 0 7110 2739 0

Published by Ian Allan Publishing

an imprint of Ian Allan Publishing Ltd, Terminal
House, Shepperton, Surrey TW17 8AS.
Printed by Ian Allan Printing Ltd, Riverdene
Business Park, Hersham, Surrey KT12 4RG.

Code: 0011/B2

Title page: Underground trains have the ability
to take substantial changes in line geometry
in their stride. This is the view looking north
from Brent Cross on 21 March 2000, with a
1995 stock train approaching. The brightness
of the sunshine makes the destination and
whether it goes via Bank or Charing Cross
almost unreadable. *John Glover*

Bibliography

The range of works on this subject is not large. Pride of place must go to *Handling London's Underground Traffic* by J. P. Thomas, the then Operating Manager. Published as long ago as 1928, this book offers an extensive discussion of the scene nearly three-quarters of a century ago.

Of a similar age, but also useful, is *Underground Railways* by Vernon Somerfield. Published by Thomas Nelson in 1934, it offers interesting descriptions of matters such as guards taking over from gatemen, when compressed air replaced manual train door operation.

American practice features strongly in *Urban Rail Transit, Its Economics and Technology*, A. Scheffer Lang and Richard M. Soberman, MIT Press, Cambridge, MA, 1964.

Of more recent date is *Rail Transit Capacity* (ISBN 0 309 05718 3), a report for the Transport Research Board by Tom Parkinson and Ian Fisher, National Academy Press, Washington DC, 1996.

For railway safety matters, readers are referred to the series of *Railway Safety Principles and Guidance* documents published by HMRI, of which *Part 1* sets out the general principles and *Part 2* detailed guidance in the various areas. Of relevance to London Underground in Part 2 are 'Section A: Infrastructure', 'Section B: Stations', 'Section C: Electric Traction Systems', 'Section D: Signalling' and 'Section F: Trains'.

Various issues of *Public Transport International*, the journal of the Union Internationale des Transports Publiques (UITP) have also been consulted, and both the UITP library and that of the Institute of Logistics and Transport were able to provide me with a number of useful references. The Permanent Way Institution also provided some helpful offerings.

Contents

Bibliography	4
Acknowledgements	5
Introduction	7
1. The Underground Today	8
2. Principles of Operation	22
3. Long-standing Problems	28
4. The Trains Themselves	39
5. Timetable Compilation	58
6. Service Provision	80
7. A Simple Railway	100
8. The Stations	108
9. Performance and Infrastructure	130
10. Operational Safety	148
11. Conclusions	157
Appendix I.	160
Underground Stations 500m or Less Apart	
Appendix II.	160
Adjacent Underground Stations More Than 2,250m Apart	

Acknowledgements

My thanks are due to a number of people, in particular Malcolm Dymott of Infraco SSL, for his thoughts on what is involved in moving to substantially higher levels of train frequency, and for his extensive knowledge of the Underground system and his willingness to share it. I am also grateful to Colin Gray, Urban Railway Operations consultant, for his long and detailed critique. The discussion on railway safety owes much to Andrew Evans, London Transport Professor of Transport Safety, for his presentation to UITP British members, and to John Curley, Railtrack's Director of Performance, for his exposition to the Railway Study Association. Thanks also to Nick Agnew and to other LUL staff who have contributed in one way or another.

Introduction

This book is an exploration of some of the operational issues which are an intrinsic part of running a railway system, specifically London Underground. It builds upon the author's earlier work *abc Railway Operations*, published by Ian Allan, 1999, but dense and specialised urban networks, such as the Underground, have problems all of their own.

London Underground is a major component of the capital's well-being; after nearly a century and a half of service, it is now carrying more passengers than ever before. This is due at least in part to the extensions of the network; the most recent of these was the Jubilee Line extension to Stratford, the opening of which was completed in the closing days of 1999.

Undertakings such as this are, however, only as good as the service that they can offer the travelling public — over 900 million of them each year. This requires engineering, planning and business skills, but the operators' contributions, which have so often gone unnoticed in recent years, are also of crucial importance. This book attempts to redress that balance by setting out the basics of Underground operation. It is hoped that it will be of use to practitioners and students of the subject alike, especially to those studying for the professional examinations of the Institute of Logistics and Transport.

It seems that passenger growth is likely to continue into the future. This book concentrates on making the most out of the system that we have, but the demand for more travel cannot be met indefinitely by fine tuning the present system.

The Underground enters a new era with the creation of Transport *for* London — one of the executive agencies set up for the new London Mayor's administration which oversees the co-ordination of transport provision. It is to be hoped that new opportunities will arise as a result and that the Underground will be made more fit for its purpose as the years progress. But this is not to suggest that matters have been static in recent years. As Sir Alastair Morton said in late 1999, when paying tribute to the retiring Chief Executive of London Transport and former Managing Director of the Underground, Denis Tunnicliffe: 'He has been an outstanding operator of LUL, maintaining and renewing capacity within very limited means while getting more and more passengers on to his network.'

The need to do more with less will not change overnight, and the author trusts that this book will be of some small assistance to those who have to make it happen.

Top left: A train of C stock shows off its capability of four pairs of doors per side as it pauses at Farringdon with an inner rail Circle Line service. *John Glover*

Left: The bull's-eye symbol looks remarkably aged when presented, at it is here, in an entrance to Aldgate East station. This is 16 March 2000, but the station dates from 1938, and there is every indication that this was one of the original signs. *John Glover*

1. The Underground Today

First, a brief introduction to the Underground itself. For the past 15 years, London Underground Ltd (LUL) has been a wholly-owned subsidiary of London Transport; the company began trading on 1 April 1985. It is a nationalised industry whose powers and duties are set out in the London Regional Transport Act 1984. The LUL that this Act created is a vertically integrated railway, owning and operating the system's infrastructure and rolling stock, albeit there is some limited operation over lines owned by Railtrack PLC on the National Railways network. Likewise, a few of the stations served are operated by one of the Train Operating Companies (TOCs).

The Underground serves 275 stations, of which all but 22 are owned and operated by LUL. The system covers 408 route kilometres, of which less than one half is actually in tunnel. Sections in tunnel predominate in central London, which is the only part of the system that many passengers see. Elsewhere, the situation

changes; there are, for instance, no tunnels at all on the Metropolitan or Jubilee lines north of Finchley Road on the long climb to the Chilterns, save only one of 80m on the little-used Watford North Curve. Similarly, there are none east of Bow Road, District Line or west of White City, Central Line.

There are 12 lines which make up the Underground system, split between the sub-surface lines and the deep-level tubes. Each has been given its own colour, for publicity purposes. They divide as follows:

Sub-surface Lines:
- Circle
- District
- East London
- Hammersmith & City
- Metropolitan

The urban sections of these were constructed mainly by cut-and-cover methods, in which a trench is dug in the ground. The cutting sides are supported and lined with bricks. Tracks are laid and, in most cases, the railway is then roofed in with roads or commercial developments above. The average depth below ground level is seven metres. All the original construction from 1863 onwards was of this nature, and the present sub-surface system was virtually complete by 1918. Only minor extensions such as the line from Moor Park to Watford (Metropolitan) remained to be completed, in this case in 1925.

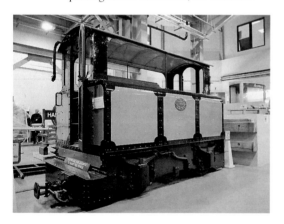

Above: An original locomotive from the City & South London Railway survives, now in the care of the London Transport Museum, where it was photographed on 6 February 2000. These locomotives were truly diminutive. *John Glover*

Above: On one of the last sections of track to be built for the surface lines, Croxley station opened on 2 November 1925. This was a joint venture between the Metropolitan Railway and the London & North Eastern Railway, the latter having inherited the obligations of its Great Central constituent. The interests of the LNER did not survive long, as far as the practical matter of running trains was concerned; this quickly became the responsibility of what is now the Metropolitan Line. This photograph was taken on 18 April 1998. *John Glover*

Tube Lines:

- Bakerloo
- Central
- Jubilee
- Northern
- Piccadilly
- Victoria
- Waterloo & City

The first tube line to be constructed, the City & South London, opened in 1890 between King William Street in the City and Stockwell. It was the first part of what was later to become the Northern Line. With the problems associated with tube railways of tunnelling, electric traction and passenger access now effectively solved, their construction proceeded apace. This was a particular feature of the Edwardian era. By the end of World War 1, a little over one quarter of the present network

was in place. Much deeper than the sub-surface lines, the average distance of tube lines below ground level is 25 metres.

The system was extended with new construction into the suburbs in the interwar years, and this also included the taking over of some of the branches of the main line railways, notably those of the London & North Eastern Railway. This was a major network expansion, and the results of those active years (and the postwar completion of some of the works which were postponed by the 1939-45 hostilities) account in total for half of the present network.

Subsequent expansion has been much more modest. The last half-century saw the end of the Underground's push to new suburban areas. Inner London needs resulted eventually in the building of the completely new Victoria Line (opened

Above: The Bakerloo Line was extended over the electric lines to Watford Junction in a service provided jointly with, latterly, the London Midland Region of British Railways. North of Queen's Park this operates today over Railtrack lines and no further than Harrow & Wealdstone. A 1972 stock train leaves Willesden Junction for Elephant & Castle on 27 October 1998. *John Glover*

1968-72) and the creation of the Jubilee Line in two stages. Opening from Baker Street to Charing Cross took place in 1969, to be followed 30 years later by the effective abandonment of the last section into Charing Cross. This was replaced by the extension via London Bridge to Docklands and to Stratford.

The growth of the Underground is shown below:

Sections of line are classified in terms of the traffic for which they were built, rather than what they are used for today. Also, lines that have subsequently been closed altogether (as in Holborn-Aldwych) or on which Underground trains no

longer run (Amersham-Aylesbury) have been omitted.

Underground Statistics

The Underground's train services are provided by a fleet of nearly 4,000 cars, which are formed mostly into trains of six, seven or eight vehicles, according to line. Both the East London and the Waterloo & City lines are operated with four-car trains only though both could take five-car trains of 53ft cars, given a few alterations to OPO mirrors and signalling. The fleet, which had been inflated in numbers temporarily by the delivery of new tube stock while at least some of the previous

Underground System Construction (Route km)							
	1863-99	1900-18	1919-34	1935-49	1950-99	Total	%
Sub-surface	106.64	49.42	3.31	1.01	–	160.38	38.2
Tube	6.30	67.93	51.93	79.43	54.09	259.68	61.8
Total	112.94	117.35	55.24	80.44	54.09	420.06	100
%	27	28	13	19	13	100	

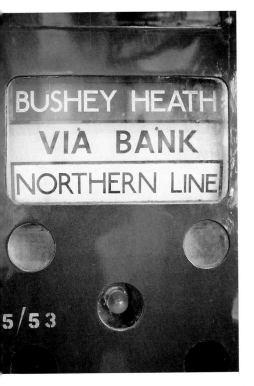

fleets were still in operation, provides over 60 million train km of service a year. The nominal track voltage is 630V dc.

Commercially, 927 million passenger journeys were made on the Underground in 1999/2000; with an average journey length of around 7.74km, this equates to a total of 7,171 million passenger km. Somewhere between 2½ and 3 million journeys are made on the Underground every working day. This is big business. Measured in terms of journeys made, rather than their length, this is comparable with those made on the whole of the National Railways system. The Underground thus forms a very important part of London's social and economic fabric. To say that London cannot do without it is perhaps an overstatement, but life would be very different (and probably much nastier) if this were attempted.

The next table (*below*) shows some key measures which, together, give a good indication of the relative importance of each line.

Underground Line Statistics

	Length	No stations served	Passengers millions pa	Av journey length
Sub-surface Lines				
Circle	21km	27	67	4.7km
District	64km	60	181	5.8km
East London	8km	8	6	n/a
Hammersmith & City	27km	28	43	4.7km
Metropolitan	67km	34	54	10.8km
Tube Lines				
Bakerloo	23km	25	84	3.5km
Central	74km	49	156	6.9km
Jubilee	38km	27	59	5.6km
Northern	58km	51	184	5.3km
Piccadilly	71km	52	174	7.7km
Victoria	21km	16	142	5.5km
Waterloo & City	2km	2	12	2.3km

Above: The Central Line extensions took over the Great Eastern's branch to Epping and Ongar. Leyton station, seen here on 15 March 2000, clearly had a new front grafted on to the GE original to suit the new image. The Central Line reached Leyton on 5 May 1947. Although the road carries frequent bus services, anywhere near the station is not considered a suitable place to stop. *John Glover*

Top right: The Victoria Line's 1967 stock looked smart in its aluminium unpainted livery, until the aerosols began to get to work on it. The train on the right is arriving at Northumberland Park depot, that on the left departing to run on the line. *John Glover*

Collectively, these figures demonstrate the huge importance of the Northern, District, Piccadilly and Central lines in terms of passenger numbers, though it may be noted that the relatively short Victoria Line comes in very close behind the 'big four'. It also achieves this with many fewer trains.

Passenger numbers are a summation of those originating on the line in question, plus those interchanging from other lines. One third of all Underground journeys made require one interchange, and another 4% require two (or more). The total of the journeys made on each line thus exceeds the number of end-to-end passenger journeys made on the system as a whole. It may be noted that this is mostly 1996 data; that for the Jubilee Line passengers relates to the Stanmore-Charing Cross service only, without the benefit of the 1999 Stratford extension.

Passenger numbers, it should be added, are not a straight proxy for revenue earned, which is broadly related to distance travelled. On the Metropolitan Line, in particular, the average journey distance of 10.8km is much higher than the norm; the next highest is the Piccadilly at 7.7km. Besides being a long line in its own right, the Piccadilly also has the major traffic generator of Heathrow Airport at one end.

The figures are not summed, as this would involve much double counting; for instance, the Circle Line is not the exclusive provider of services at any station. Nevertheless, they do give an idea of where the strengths and the weaknesses lie.

Right: The last few commuters await the arrival of their train to Morden via Bank at Hendon Central on Tuesday 21 March 2000. There is often a slight hiatus in passengers joining between 09.00 or thereabouts and 09.30, when the One-Day Travelcard becomes available. *John Glover*

Above: Mirrors and CCTV screens are provided at Acton Town to assist opo (one-person operation) drivers on the westbound Piccadilly Line platforms, seen here on 6 February 2000. *John Glover*

The Passengers

Who are the passengers? Briefly, they are in the professional and middle class socio-economic groups and 90% are between the ages of 20 and 60. Those under the age of 35 are particularly well represented. They might be thought of as those who are likely to look for service quality, while their relative affluence makes them able to afford it.

In a similar vein, 35% of Underground journeys are made wholly within Zone 1, 50% between Zone 1 and one of the other zones, and 15% wholly within Zones 2 to 6. Those travelling only in Zone 1 as far as the Underground is concerned will include most of those passengers whose journeys start or finish on National Railways.

The Underground Business

Unlike most businesses, London Transport's objective is not to maximise profits or returns on investment. This is because:

- The benefits of public transport are felt much more widely than by its customers alone and include lower road traffic congestion, reduced accidents and pollution, and a contribution to the efficient operation of London's economy.
- The benefits of improvements in services delivered to customers cannot all be recovered in fare revenue because fare levels are regulated to provide social benefits.

London Underground's company objective, therefore, is: 'To maximise net social benefit within available funds and subject to a defined gross margin'. This leads to a strategy of increasing market share by stimulating (and retaining) new Underground travel, and to make existing customers more satisfied with the service provided. Such objectives do change. Under the GLC, the Underground was to maximise passenger miles within an agreed financial target.

How do customers view the value of service improvements? The following list suggests the topic areas which might be identified as areas for investment:

- Train frequency
- Train reliability
- Train security
- Train condition
- Train information
- Train environment
- Station security/staff
- Station condition
- Station information
- Station environment
- Station facilities
- Station access.

The operations of London Underground have to satisfy a wide range

Above: The sharing of premises is slowly on the increase. At West Brompton, an Edgware Road to Wimbledon train of C stock is arriving. On the left, behind the stout fence, are the platforms on Railtrack's West London line; the footbridge can be seen in the background. *John Glover*

of people. At a basic level, the service consists of getting the customer from his point of entry to the system to his point of exit as quickly as possible. To fail on this is to fail completely. But there is more to it: the availability of information, the general cleanliness both on the station and the train, the smartness of the whole are all part of the service offered. Nobody wants to pass through scruffy ticket office areas and ride in a smelly train covered in graffiti and knee deep in litter.

Different customer groups have different needs, although they all use the same stations and the same trains. The commuters are not interested in basic information about Underground services; they already know all that they need to know about their journey. They definitely do not want seats sacrificed for luggage racks in trains. The tourist or occasional visitor, however, is looking for reassurance that they are in the right place, and where

if at all they will need to change trains. They also want somewhere to place their bags. Such contrasts can be seen any day on journeys between central London and Piccadilly Line Heathrow stations, and they do not make for domestic and international harmony.

Other groups, such as infrequent travellers, value train cleanliness, environment and security more than regular customers, and women value such matters more highly than men. Also, the under 25s and the over 60s value improvements more highly than regular customers.

Investment in service improvements needs to take into account the variation in needs of these contrasting groups, and others. It must not be assumed that what is good for one is necessarily good for all.

Extensive market research exercises are undertaken to explore the areas described. These seek to answer

Top left: The railway needs continued maintenance, as this view of Shadwell station on the East London Line shows. The supporting scaffolding is beyond the area needed for passenger access to trains. This view dates from 16 December 1998, and is among the types of work undertaken by the Infracos. *John Glover*

Above: Advertising livery for Underground trains made its debut on 19 June 1995 with this train of Piccadilly Line 1973 stock painted in the colours of United Airlines. This picture was taken at Acton Town as the train was about to enter public service. *John Glover*

questions such as how much it is worth spending on stations. What would customers be prepared to pay for moving from a situation in which stations are described as 'very grubby and dirty overall' to 'some dirty areas'? Or is it worth spending more to move to 'reasonably clean everywhere' or even 'spotlessly clean everywhere'.

This does not mean that fares should be raised to pay for such work. The aim rather is to maximise social benefit from moneys spent, as discussed earlier in this section. It is to make certain that what London Underground might do in the way of optional investment in the system is indeed seen by its customers as a worthwhile benefit. Similar investigations were used to justify the extensive refurbishment programmes for many tube and sub-surface train stocks.

Organisation

While the Underground undoubtedly has its niche in the well-being of the capital, the means by which the undertaking is organised are by no means settled permanently. From the creation of the London Passenger Transport Board in 1933, major reorganisations have taken place in 1948 (nationalisation as the London Transport Executive), 1963 (creation of a separate London Transport Board), 1969 (municipalisation under the Greater London Council) and 1984 (nationalisation again under London Regional Transport). The first four of these reorganisations each lasted an average of 13 years, so a further

Left: The Jubilee Line was in operation at Stratford on 25 May 1999, but only for testing purposes. A pair of 1996 stock trains are seen in the almost complete station. *John Glover*

Above left: The installation of ticket gates is now almost universal on London Underground. A straight line of eight gates is installed here at Bermondsey, Jubilee Line; the ticket office and help points are on the right. Notably, this photograph was taken from the public pavement, outside the station. The date is 15 March 2000. *John Glover*

Above: Guards are no longer used on passenger trains anywhere on London Underground. Helpful information was being dispensed here at Bank on a southbound 1959 stock Northern Line train. *John Glover*

attempt was perhaps overdue. And so it proved. On 20 March 1998, the Deputy Prime Minister John Prescott announced a Public/Private Partnership (PPP) approach. Train operation and the interface with the consumer were to remain the responsibility of London Underground, which will also retain the freehold of the infrastructure. The maintenance, renewal and investment in new infrastructure and rolling stock will be undertaken by the private sector under contract to LU, which itself is to be transferred to the Greater London Authority.

It will be a matter for the private sector to finance these tasks, to be paid for by the income stream from fares and financial support from Government in recognition of the external social and economic benefits of the Underground. The three 'Infracos' (infrastructure companies created from the existing LUL organisation) were arranged as follows:

BCV   Bakerloo, Central (including
          Waterloo & City) and Victoria lines
JNP   Jubilee, Northern and
          Piccadilly lines
SSL   All sub-surface lines.

Left: Traffic on the Jubilee Line extension built up quickly. Commuters leave the station at Canary Wharf on the morning of 25 November 1999, at which stage the last elements were still to open. *John Glover*

Above: The East London Line may become part of the National Railways network and one day see through trains from Wimbledon or West Croydon to Highbury & Islington and Finsbury Park. In the meantime, it is a preserve of four-car sets of A stock, one of which is seen approaching Surrey Quays from the south. *John Glover*

The Infraco contractors are expected to deliver £7 billion worth of investment, at 1998 prices, over a 15-year period, though the length of the maintenance contracts themselves may exceed this.

There are a number of key differences compared with the privatisation of British Rail:

- The freehold of the infrastructure remains in public ownership.
- There are no plans for on-track competition from other train operators.
- The operation of signalling and the management of the timetable remains with LU.
- LU will have overall responsibility for safety.

This brief recapitulation of the Government's reorganisation of London Underground is provided as a background to its operation in the new century, but it is London Underground's operations

Above: The complex junctions at Leytonstone allow for the original main line from Epping, centre, to be joined by the branch from Hainault. This is from where the 1962 stock train is approaching; the beginning of a descent of the eastbound line to a tunnel mouth is seen on the left. If the Chelsea-Hackney line is ever built, this would take over the Epping route, and the Central Line would proceed to Hainault only. *John Glover*

today which form the main subject of this book. Until contracts are signed, the details of the approach on infrastructure may well change; on the operational front, the influence of the Mayor for London and his objectives will only become clear after a period of time in office.

What will the Mayor actually do? As set out by the Department of the Environment, Transport and the Regions, the Mayor will:

- Be a strong voice, speaking for the whole of London.
- Plan for the future and set out a budget.
- Run new transport and economic development bodies.
- Work with a new Metropolitan Police Authority.
- Organise London-wide action to improve the environment.

- Oversee a new Fire Authority.
- Organise action on other issues, such as a bid for the Olympics.

Four executive agencies have been set up, one of which is Transport *for* London (T*f*L). One of the Mayor's key roles is to oversee the co-ordination of transport provision. T*f*L's Chairman, either the Mayor or an appointee, is responsible for appointing the T*f*L Board of eight to 15 Members. T*f*L's duties include those exercised previously by London Transport, but also the functions of bodies such as the Docklands Light Railway, the Public Carriage Office, the Traffic Director for London, and others. However, control of London Underground Ltd remains with the Government until after the Public/Private Partnership contracts have been signed.

2. Principles of Operation

Before proceeding further, however, it is perhaps worth while to set out what the author considers to be the 12 basic principles involved in railway operations, as they might be adapted for the London Underground environment. Many of the points made here will be met again in various guises elsewhere in the book.

1. The service which London Underground provides and for which it is paid by customers is movement.

The key test of a public transport system is its ability to deliver the customer to his or her destination, in as short a time as is reasonably possible. Smart stations, freedom from litter and spruced-up trains are to be commended, but the main business purpose is to get people to where they want to go. Failure to do so is total failure.

2. Faster journey times allow the same rolling stock and staff to provide a more frequent service.

The more polished the operation throughout, the greater the service throughput that is possible. If train times for a 60min end-to-end journey can be cut to 55min, the round trip will be 10min faster and equal to an 8.3% productivity improvement. Over the service as a whole, this can provide additional train crews and trains which can then be used to augment the service. This does not require capital expenditure.

3. Load factors are all-important.

Carrying empty space around is not the basis on which fortunes are made. While an element of empty running is unavoidable for positioning rolling stock and train crew, the aim must always be to fill the trains with paying customers. A production manager who maximises the train/km run within whatever constraints that exist is doing a good job, but from a company point of view it is of little benefit if load factors are poor.

4. Peak demand is difficult to cater for economically.

Ideally, business assets should be used for a large proportion of each and every day. Any assets which are used for two short periods only, five days a week, are unlikely to earn their keep unless premium charges can be exacted from customers for their use. Where there are step changes in asset requirements, as for instance when line capacity is saturated for a highly peaked operation and additional running lines are necessary, only public authorities are likely to be able to justify the expenditure.

5. Rail traffics are interdependent.

Where the running lines are used by a mixture of stopping and non-stopping services, more capacity can be made available by minimising the speed and time differentials. If the objective is to maximise the throughput of trains, this is most readily achieved by all having similar performance and all having the same stopping pattern. Such objectives, though, may be at variance with the needs of the market.

6. Line capacity is a scarce resource.

If the line is fully occupied, no more

Above: Shoe on conductor rail is the basis of current pick up, as demonstrated here on a 1938 stock car in the London Transport Museum, 22 July 1999. *John Glover*

trains can be run, whatever the market might want. However, are there alternatives for using the existing line capacity more productively, by running longer trains, for instance? Is there scope for introducing grade-separated junctions to minimise conflicts? Is the present service pattern right for the circumstances?

7. Short turnrounds are a key to utilisation.

At Elephant & Castle, Bakerloo Line, or at Brixton or Walthamstow Central on the Victoria Line, there is only a single-island platform for terminating trains. Incoming trains will sometimes conflict with departing trains at the crossover outside the station. This all puts a premium on slick operation. A third platform, as at

Left: Canada Water station is completely new, with platforms on both the East London and Jubilee lines. This is only 320m from Rotherhithe station; presumably it was not considered practical to reroute the Jubilee Line to that extent. The station has been provided with comprehensive bus interchange facilities, as seen here on 20 March 2000. *John Glover*

ENTERING THE TRAIN.

37.

CENT

J.H.L.

Trains every few minutes.
No worry about catching them.

Above: How simple it all was on the Central London Railway! This is from a display in the London Transport Museum. *John Glover*

High Barnet (Northern Line) or Uxbridge (Metropolitan Line) may be helpful, especially for smoothing out service irregularities.

8. Good performance is vital.
However good the timetable may look on paper, putting it into operation is another matter. The art here is to produce an economical service which is challenging to management and staff, but without it being almost impossible to achieve except when everything is going perfectly. This virtually never happens, and the result is disheartenment and a 'Why bother?' response. To build in some judicious slack, but not too much, is essential. Computerised timetable production is indeed practicable, but it needs an experienced (human) timetable compiler to put the finishing touches to it.

9. Surplus facilities may be an embarrassment.
Spare capacity is a drain on company resources, which can be and often should be avoided. This is true whether it refers to track, trains or facilities. On the other hand, the future is uncertain, and an asset once disposed of may be more than a little difficult to reinstate. Most obviously, this might refer to the lifting of track and a subsequent land sale. Is there, in fact, an alternative use? Readers might wish to ponder on the future of the Charing Cross terminus, Jubilee Line. To keep this usable requires maintenance, and what about the escalators? Could they be installed elsewhere?

10. The customers are the best judge of what they want.
What *do* customers want? Is there a trade-

Above: District Line trains at Richmond on 5 December 1998 consisted of a pair of D stocks. The benefits of a uniform fleet are considerable, since all have identical capacity, performance, etc. Unfortunately, the District still has to use C stock for the Edgware Road service. *John Glover*

off between seats and standing on trains? How do service regularity, frequency, station services, ease of ticketing and all the other components of a journey rate in the eyes of the customer? There is unlikely to be a single answer, since customer profiles differ. Holders of period Travelcards use them overwhelmingly for work or education purposes; the most popular uses of the one-day Travelcard are for social purposes and shopping. Why do men use the Underground more than women, while on buses it is the other way round? Seventy one percent of Underground users are in the ABC1 social groups; this falls to 48% for bus users. Overseas visitors are responsible for as much as 9% of Underground trips, and this is overwhelmingly their principal choice of travel mode. The operator needs to plan the service as best he can, but with

a view to the likely business needs and meeting the wishes of the customers.

11. The railway does not exist in a vacuum.

Hardly surprisingly, those who live within five minutes' walk of an Underground station make more use of it than those who live further away. However, the distance between stations always means that rail access often requires a second mode to reach the station. Almost three-quarters of Underground users walk to the station, but 10% come by bus and 6% by car. These are system-wide figures; 41% of Manor House passengers come by bus, and 53% reach Epping by car. The other major mode used is main line rail, which accounts for 66% of Underground passengers at Waterloo. It might be added that 3% of Piccadilly

Line passengers come by 'other' feeder mode; could this be aircraft? The use of a feeder mode and interchange needs to be encouraged, something which is now becoming more apparent on the National Railways network.

12. Change takes time.

Finally, new timetables are not manufactured overnight; they take time to put together and implement. When they are introduced, they are also likely to take time to bed down. Staff need to become accustomed to the changes before they can be fully confident in their ability to deliver. Regular passengers also take time to adjust. There is nothing wrong with change, but a little time is needed.

Above: Sloane Square station was seriously damaged in World War 2 and has lost much of its roof. For many years, it was well known for having a bar on its platform, one of the last stations to do so. The D stock is the basic service provider here; this picture was taken on 19 December 1998. *John Glover*

Left: Interchange is easy when trains are so close, but be warned! The doors of the Class 165 were released only on the eastbound (right-hand) side here at Greenford, so passengers could easily be mistaken. The Thames Trains unit forms a service to Paddington on 19 December 1998. *John Glover*

3. Long-standing Problems

It may be thought that the operational problems of the Underground, in trying to fit in as many trains (and therefore as much capacity as possible), have always been there. Yet in the very earliest days, the success of the undertaking was by no means assured. This was as much to do with doubters in the civil engineering professions as others. They told the company directors of the yet-to-be-constructed first stage of the Metropolitan, between Paddington and Farringdon, that it could not be built. Furthermore, if they managed to build it, they could not operate it, and even if they overcame that hurdle nobody would travel on it. It opened in 1863 and quickly became a success.

Yet this encouraging advice was given in respect of what was in many ways a conventional steam railway. The first tube railway, the City & South London of 1890, was originally to have been cable hauled, since the newfangled electric traction had yet to prove itself. In the deep tunnels where it was to be constructed, the problems of excavating the tunnels (by shield) also had to be solved, while means

Below: The London Underground Electric Railways, or as it is better known UERL (same words, different order), had its own exciting motif, as seen here displayed at the London Transport Museum on 22 July 1999. *John Glover*

Above: A Piccadilly Line train of refurbished 1973 stock runs eastbound at speed through Chiswick Park on 17 December 1998, passing a D stock District Line train in the platform here. This is one of the few instances on the Underground today where both fast and stopping trains run side by side — but not on the same tracks. This photograph also shows the extent of the difference in body dimensions between the two. *John Glover*

had to be found for passengers to access the deep-level platforms. Lifts at each station were the first major application of that technology; escalators came later.

In such a pioneering situation, the niceties of planning for high capacity were probably not given the attention which they were later shown to require. After all, if the pundits claim that the whole venture is impossible to carry out, there is little point in arguing over whether the works should provide for four- or five-car trains anyway. Business success was by no means guaranteed; the promoters would have been well justified in looking for minimum-cost solutions.

An Early View

By World War 1, all the Underground lines now in existence in central London had been constructed, excepting only the Victoria and Jubilee lines. A paper presented by W. E. Blake, Superintendent of the Line, Underground Electric Railways of London (UERL) in 1918 described the operational problems then apparent and how they were tackled under busy wartime conditions. It is discussed here at length, since it sheds an interesting light on what turned out to be some very long-standing difficulties. Present names of lines are used throughout, but the emphasis is on the District.

Train Length

The District Line stations could accommodate eight-car trains, but only by running the front half of the first car into the tunnel and leaving the last half of the last car also in the tunnel. Platforms were lengthened by reconstructing the platform end ramps. Effectively, this made the ramps horizontal, with the result that they provided a narrow ledge for alighting passengers at such stations.

'More by accident than design' it had been found out that platforms could be lengthened at some of the busier points,

including the open-air sections. An experimental nine-car train had been introduced in June 1914, in which trains from Ealing Broadway to the City would have the rear vehicle restricted to passengers joining at stations to Hammersmith and then alighting only at either Embankment or Mansion House. Staffing difficulties in finding men to look after the last car and ensure that passengers did not try to alight elsewhere, at all of which the platforms were too short, meant that the experiment was discontinued for the duration. It was said to have caught on well with the public.

Detailed surveys had showed that it was possible to lengthen some platforms to accommodate 10 cars, in the same way that the tunnel stations could be made to accommodate eight-car trains.

Joining and Splitting Trains

The District Line ran over the tracks of the London, Tilbury & Southend Railway (LT&S) from Campbell Road Junction (east of Bow Road) to Barking. This meant that the line capacity available to the District was less here than it was west of Whitechapel towards Earl's Court, where the District had control. However, although the company had to run fewer trains to Barking than it might have

wished, train length was less restricted because of the length of the Tilbury's platforms. West of Whitechapel, platform lengths dictated short trains, but more trains in total could be accommodated. The District's response was to run the two busiest trains of the day from East Ham (both at around 08.00) as 10-cars, or even 11-cars, and split them into two separate trains at Whitechapel.

Service Frequency

During the busiest peak hour, the District was then running a remarkable 43 trains per hour (tph). 'This meant,' said Blake, 'that an average interval of 84 seconds must not be exceeded between the departure of successive trains from a station.' The through services in terms of trains per hour during the 'rush' period were then comprised as follows:

Circle	10	Richmond	6
Wimbledon	10	Ealing Broadway	10
Putney line	2	Hounslow	4
South Harrow	1		

There were also additional local services, which did not venture on to the south side of the Circle:

Putney line	10	South Harrow	5
Hounslow	6	Uxbridge	2

It would seem that 'Putney line' meant trains terminating at Putney Bridge, but this is not stated explicitly. Rush period service frequencies given for other lines were:

- Piccadilly: 24tph, plus 15tph for Holborn to Aldwych;
- Hampstead tube: 19tph to Archway and 19tph to Golders Green (these were both from Charing Cross as the connection to the City & South London Railway at Euston had yet to be made);
- City & South London: 25tph, and
- Central: 24tph.

Some calculations followed.

Below: District Line R stock pre-dated World War 2. In the general approach there are similarities with the 1938 tube stock, though the overall impression was more spacious. *John Glover*

It had been found that the time taken between making the brake application and bringing a District Line train to rest was 12sec. The corresponding time taken for starting a train and attaining maximum speed was between 30sec and 36sec. About 20sec of the acceleration time was spent in clearing the starting signal. Now, if the station stop time was 30sec, at 43tph there were only 54sec available between one train starting and the next train stopping. The need for station work to be completed quickly was therefore underlined.

When the District Railway was first automatically signalled, said Blake, the home signal was placed at a minimum distance of 400ft (145m) on the approach side of the station. A second home signal was added very shortly afterwards at all the stations in the congested area. Thus, immediately after the train that was at the station started and proceeded for a certain distance out of the station, the second train was able to come forward, still maintaining a safe distance between trains. In the same way, a third home signal was afterwards provided at the busiest stations, where, owing to the density of the traffic, the stops were longer than at the others.

Tube Stock Design
The inadequacies of the tube gate stock, with only one entry/exit point at each end of the vehicle, were next considered. This was causing crowds to form on the platform around the doors, which was a problem in itself as it made it difficult for passengers to leave the train. A central door on each car was considered highly desirable, though Blake thought that platform curvature and gaps between platform and train would be a real problem here. Quite why it was not seen as an equivalent problem at the car ends was not explained. This may have been merely because many of the worst platforms, eg Waterloo, Bakerloo, were on the outside of the curves rather than the inside.

Above: Passengers try to board a C stock train for Edgware Road at Earl's Court on 22 July 1999. There appear to be a couple of bicycles waiting to board. It is stations like this where the time can so easily be lost. *John Glover*

Platform Queues

Based on New York experience, barriers were erected on the Bakerloo Line at Oxford Circus and Embankment, to force joining passengers to wait until alighting passengers had left the carriage. However, this required the train drivers to stop every time almost exactly at a fixed point on the platform.

An experiment to see whether a queuing system would work was tried out at Knightsbridge on the westbound Piccadilly Line platform during the evening peak. Provided the driver stopped at the appointed place, the platform would be clear for those alighting, and passengers would enter the train in the order in which they joined the queue. While it worked quite well at Knightsbridge, it was found that there wasn't really sufficient room on the platform even at this relatively lightly used station, and at least one additional member of platform staff was needed to police the system.

Station Stop Times

These had extended during World War 1, and the reason was said to be the greater use of the system by 'inexperienced travellers, who are not so quick at entering and alighting and who stand in the doorways, necessitating [other] passengers pushing by them, instead of getting out of the way'. Mass tourism had yet to make its presence felt!

Blake also criticised station designers who placed successive platform entrances and exits at one end of the platform, which resulted in that end of the trains being very full while the rest could be relatively lightly loaded. Although no line was mentioned, stations from Barons Court eastwards on the Piccadilly do suffer from this today. 'Pass along the platform, please' thus has a long pedigree.

According to Blake, in those days it took about 1½ min to unload and load a 39-seat bus. If trains with a total capacity of around 800 took as long as this at stations, he said, 'the maximum service would be reduced to about 26 trains an hour, whereas 43 are actually scheduled'.

Non-stopping of Trains

Non-stopping trains were established on the District in 1907, with the following advantages:

- Overall journey times were shortened, with the journey itself more comfortable and less monotonous for passengers.
- Loading between trains was better equalised, since a busy train could have some stops eliminated and the traffic for those stations dealt with by other trains.
- Operating costs were reduced as less current was being taken through fewer accelerations away from stops, while faster end-to-end journey times led to the possibility of fewer trains being needed to work the total service.

The principle was illustrated with westbound District Line services from Sloane Square towards Acton Town. The first train was a Wimbledon service (Train A), which diverged from the main route at Earl's Court. If this was followed by a Circle Line service (Train B), this would in those days have used a separate track from South Kensington onwards. Loss of these trains created an opening for the following train (Train C) to run nonstop from Sloane Square right through to Hammersmith, omitting the five intermediate stations. After this, Train C would return to stopping at all stations. The train after this (Train D) would call at all stations to Hammersmith, and then run nonstop to Turnham Green, omitting two stations.

This also had the effect of separating train arrivals at Turnham Green. Train C would be sufficiently faster so that it took up the train slot that would otherwise have been used by Train A had it continued towards Hammersmith, while Train D omitted fewer stops and was thus able to take up the train path vacated by Train C.

Left: A train of D stock for Ealing Broadway rounds the sharp curve into West Kensington; the railway is between a major road and the block on the right. On the left, the line leads to Lillie Bridge Permanent Way depot. *John Glover*

Right: Passengers join and alight from an eastbound train of 1973 stock at North Ealing on 20 March 2000. *John Glover*

In this way, an even-interval service was maintained for Turnham Green.

Of Trains C and D, one train would then proceed to Ealing Broadway, the other to Richmond or to Hounslow. The whole sequence was then repeated.

Skip-stopping of Trains

Usually, nonstopping requires additional running lines to be fully effective; the District only managed to achieve it because of the diverging branches. Skip-stopping is a variant more appropriate to a railway with only one pair of running lines. Here, succeeding trains omit alternate quieter stations, but all stop at the busy ones. As practised on the Piccadilly, the first train would nonstop at Covent Garden, York Road (closed 1932) and Holloway Road; the second would nonstop at Russell Square, Caledonian Road and Arsenal. Both would stop at Leicester Square, Holborn, King's Cross and Finsbury Park. This approach was claimed to work well and to be appreciated by the majority of passengers; the longer the journey, the greater the benefits.

Variations on the theme elsewhere included the 4tph Bakerloo Line trains to Watford Junction, which were busier than the 24tph Queen's Park terminators. Consequently, the Watford trains were selectively nonstopped. However, being busier, their station times were longer, and this had a balancing effect on overall journey times. It was intended to introduce similar services on the (then) yet-to-be-opened Wood Lane to Ealing Broadway Central Line and Golders Green to Edgware Northern Line extensions.

Critics will, however, note that both of these schemes create difficulty for some short journeys. Thus, passengers travelling from York Road to Arsenal were required to go past their destination to Finsbury Park and then return. Alternatively, the passenger could travel via King's Cross. Also, stations that are nonstopped find their service levels reduced by one half. Nevertheless, such disadvantages may be worth accepting for the greater good of the majority.

Finally, there was an understandable desire by UERL to get across to the public how it could help the company run the trains more efficiently. This was seen to be to the advantage of everybody. There was a completely matter-of-fact approach to a theme of 'Train delays reduce the accommodation available'. No soft-touch advertising slogans here! A series of four posters was produced, stressing the following points:

• The undesirability of crowding the carriage so that the train gates cannot be shut, causing delay in starting.

- Crowding round the gangway impeded passengers who wished to alight, thereby impeding the entry of those on the platform.
- The need for passengers to pass down the cars and not obstruct the entrances.
- The need for hurry.

With small variations, such as the substitution of train doors for train gates, the same is true today, nearly a century later. Over that period, manual operation, by gateman or passenger, was replaced by power doors. Passenger door control with push buttons was in vogue in the 1940s and 1950s, but was dropped because of unreliability. More recently, it has returned and may be found on the D stock (District Line) and tube cars from the 1992 stock onwards.

Railway Justification
Capacity is a major problem for Underground railways, which are often unable to match as fully as they might like the demands for travel placed upon them. It is also an irritant for their customers; even if they are able to join trains at the time of their choice, travelling conditions may be decidedly uncomfortable. The result is less than happy passengers, who are often only too willing to find fault with the undertaking and its management.

It is a customary view that, for instance, the Central Line runs at full capacity between Liverpool Street and Bank. Certainly, this is true to the extent that this is the busiest section of that particular line, and that loads can be excessive in the two daily peaks. During the 1950s, in the last years of the Standard-stock operation, the Liverpool Street-Bank section of the Central Line was a very serious bottleneck, and a number of features regarding operation through that section are of particular interest:

- Heavy loadings, with large proportions alighting and boarding, particularly at Liverpool Street.

Left: Three lines of commuters use the escalators at Canary Wharf on 20 March 2000 to reach the open air; all ticketing is dealt with at the intermediate lower level, which they are leaving. *John Glover*

Right: The extent of the escalators giving access to the Jubilee Line at Westminster is very noticeable in this view of 20 March 2000. It is this scale of infrastructure which is likely to be needed in many more places if growth continues apace. *John Glover*

- Inadequate doorways on trains, particularly at the centre where coupled four-car units resulted in adjacent motor cars with only one double doorway each.
- Consequent excessive peak period dwell times, westbound in the morning and eastbound in the evening, creating almost the 'inoperable' railway. In such conditions it may be impossible to run sufficient trains to carry inter-station loadings while allowing sufficient dwell time to get passengers off and on trains.
- The provision of speed-control signalling in both directions at Liverpool Street.
- In the morning peak one or two manned spare trains waited in Liverpool Street siding to cover the possibility of serious westbound gaps. (The cross-platform interchanges at Stratford and at Mile End made a late running train particularly vulnerable to station delays, and the opening up of a gap in front of it).
- The 'blocking back' from Bank in the evening eventually required 5min extra running time to be scheduled by the end of the peak, making 19min instead of 14min for the 3.47 miles, or less than 11mph! (The scheduling alternative of allowing sufficient recovery times at the terminal was impracticable because there was not enough capacity for extended layovers at the termini.)

When the Standard stock was replaced by 1959 stock, the problems suddenly changed. The main difficulty was getting people off platforms sufficiently quickly in the morning peak — particularly at Bond Street and to a lesser extent at Holborn — because of the limited number and/or width of exits.

Yet, in giving the 1993 London Transport Diamond Jubilee Lecture, Sir Francis McWilliams, Lord Mayor of London, was uncompromising in his remarks:

'There is no doubt in my mind that in terms of moving large numbers of people, public transport should be the most efficient and safest use of land. In the case of railways, and the Underground of course, the permanent way must be occupied for a good proportion of the time.

'It is a waste of resources to have large areas of land dedicated to rail travel and then to underutilise them. This is readily seen when one considers peak time travel demands with off-peak demands. Huge resources are required for providing track, signalling and trains for only limited times of the day. Throughout the remainder of the time underutilisation is prevalent.'

Sir Francis then stated, categorically, that building more roads to accommodate more traffic was not a sensible option in a dense urban, modern society.

'The very fact that railways have shown . . . that they can deliver over 860,000 people into the central area within a three-hour peak period, albeit with many standees, illustrates that the capability for additional travel is already there.

'There can be no doubt that the City relies heavily on public, particularly rail, transport. About three-quarters of the City's workforce arrive at work by Underground or suburban railway.' (There are some other, minor, options.) 'But, in the end, rail is certain to remain crucial to the viability of London's central business district.'

In essence, this is one of the major arguments in favour of the urban railway. What Sir Francis McWilliams perhaps failed to mention was that off-peak travel, especially in the West End, is also growing fast.

The Capacity Conundrum

It follows that capacity issues will never disappear, and that getting the best use out of the railway infrastructure is going to dominate thinking in the coming years as much as in the past. What are the main areas for consideration? It is suggested that these can be examined usefully under the following headings:

- The design of the trains themselves, including the length of each train.
- The frequency with which trains run and the construction of the timetable.
- The mix of train types and services on any given section of line, which may or may not be fully compatible with each other.
- The incidence of junctions on the track and the effects on the service plan.
- The stations at which the trains call, particularly in respect of access to and from station platforms.
- The track and signalling systems, which to a large extent determine service frequencies.

These topics are considered in the following chapters.

The Trains Themselves

4

The train is the most obvious part of the hardware, even if the track, signalling, power supplies, drainage, stations, depots and so on are equally important in terms of being able to deliver the service required. However, the train is the vehicle in which customers travel.

Train Specifications

A train, like any other piece of railway equipment, has to meet acceptable standards for the operators, and also for the engineers whose job it is to maintain it. It is suggested that the following attributes are the main ones sought:

- Performance
- Reliability
- Availability
- Maintainability

Each is now discussed in turn.

Performance

This is, essentially, part of the manufacturing specification. It concerns matters such as the number of traction motors, the acceleration and deceleration rates, speed capability and the rate at which things happen. Thus train doors can be made to open and close much faster, and acceleration/deceleration rates can be such as to result in standing passengers losing their balance. In both cases the overall journey times are likely to be reduced but with unacceptable side effects.

Above: The Metropolitan A stock dates from the early 1960s; in fact it is probably the largest fleet of its age still in revenue service in Britain. The three-plus-two seating is barely wide enough for real comfort, but it does make excellent use of the space available. This view was taken at Aldgate on 15 March 2000. There are not many trains on metro systems anywhere with luggage racks. *John Glover*

Broadly, today's operator can specify what he wants in performance terms; other considerations do however limit what can be achieved.

Reliability

Reliable trains are those whose failure rate is low, and this is the basis of a specification in such matters. The 'mean distance travelled between failures' is

Left: Tube stock is built up to the maximum cross-section which can be accommodated in the tunnels. As can be seen here with a southbound 1995 stock train emerging from the bore of the 1km Burroughs Tunnels at Hendon Central on 20 March 2000, the amount of space to spare is minimal. What there is has to take account of the kinematic envelope, the sway of the train at various levels of speed and of loading, the suspension and wheel diameters. These last slowly wear down until they need replacement. *John Glover*

Above: The 1992 tube stock is made up into eight-car trains for Central Line work, seen here arriving with a westbound train at Leyton on 15 March 2000. The new bridge in the background carries a footway across the railway and also across the M11 motorway, which lies directly to the left of the railway in a cutting. *John Glover*

probably the most widely used, since distance travelled is easily measured through rolling stock diagrams (and the variations which may occur). An alternative might be 'time in traffic between failures'. In reality, some equipment ages according to usage and some on a time basis. Either is simple to understand by everybody concerned and easy to apply, the main point being that just to say that the equipment must be reliable is not enough. In addition, the duty cycle of train equipment is very intensive; for example, on the C stock fleet there are a total of 1.4 million door leaf operations every day. Increasingly, such specifications are becoming part of a contract with manufacturers or others, and they must be expressed in such a manner that they are precise and not a cause of litigation in themselves. It is also highly desirable that this does not result in an

army of staff being hired merely to keep detailed records.

This, however, is only the beginning. Does a failure result in a train being unable to be moved, being taken out of service and run empty to depot, or merely some degradation in performance until the problem is corrected? On an Underground railway, the consequences of failure can be quite different from a conventional one. For example, it is merely inconvenient for the train braking system to 'fail safe' out in the open. It is a very different matter in the tube tunnel, where it is essential that any isolation necessary to enable a train to move can be undertaken from inside the train and, preferably, from the leading cab. It can be argued that any item of equipment which requires out-of-course maintenance, attention and repair could be classified as 'a failure'. Ideally, a specified failure rate

would probably be of this variety, irrespective of the consequences in terms of service interruption. Thus, a train operator might be able to live with a 'sticky door', provided it doesn't get any worse. However, if the problem manifests itself near the beginning of a journey from (say) West Ruislip to Epping, and the door requires a hefty shove from a helpful passenger to get it closed, this becomes more difficult when the train empties as it nears the terminus. The journey is also a total of 36 stations long, and even an extra 15sec per station produces a cumulative delay of 9min. True, not all the platforms are on the same side of the train, so the door will not always be used, but this just shows how quickly delays can build up. This is not the whole of the story, either. As the service gap in front of the train grows, the train itself becomes progressively more overcrowded, and this results in station stops being extended from that cause.

The situation requires intervention through regulation of the service, perhaps by holding back the trains in advance of the defective train or, in extremis, terminating some services short of destination to prevent similar problems occurring in the reverse direction.

Availability

Trains must be available for service, to meet the stock requirements of the timetable. Note that this does not mean every train in the fleet; there will always be a proportion undergoing overhaul or minor maintenance. It is also desirable to accept that accident damage is not unknown, and some cover for this may be prudent.

Allowing for the above, the question to be addressed is what fleet size should be procured for a present peak requirement of (say) 100 trains. Is a spare requirement of 10% adequate, wasteful, or unrealistically tight? This is affected by the train formation. If all cars have a coupler at each end and most have cabs, in the event of, for instance, a window being broken, it is a simple matter to exchange the one defective vehicle for a spare. However, autocouplers are potentially a significant source of failure and drivers' cabs in the middle of a train take up space which would be used for passengers. The decision on what is a sensible spares 'float' is thus not simple. When there are only a few spare trains, it can be very difficult to utilise maintenance staff efficiently and one needs very well stocked stores. In the long run, especially with a large fleet, it may well be worth purchasing extra trains. The operator wants to be in a position whereby he can require the servicing and maintenance organisation to produce the 100 trains for peak deployment every day, without fail. If his providers decide that this means that they need a fleet of 109 trains, or 111 trains, or any other number, that is their problem. Operators are there to run services, not to walk round the factories of manufacturers and decide how many of their products to put, metaphorically speaking, into their shopping trolleys.

As so often, though, there is much more to this than meets the eye. The charges paid by the operator are likely to be higher for a larger fleet than a smaller fleet. Needs also change over time, and a fleet ordered today might still be in service in 35-40 years' time. In that period, each train will have covered about 4.1 million miles in service. Who is to say whether a current peak requirement of 100 trains is going to be relevant by the year 2040? Older trains are also likely to require more maintenance attention, with this affecting their availability. One must also recognise that in a period of that length, some cars may be lost through (hopefully) minor accidents.

The extent to which maintenance can be carried out at night or outside peak periods also affects the fleet requirement.

To some extent, the ability to move trains around between lines could help solve such dilemmas, but mixed fleets are themselves not always a blessing. Did you hear the one about the platform doors and trying to use the shorter 1972 Bakerloo Line stock on the Jubilee Line . . ? It is emphasised that this example is fictional, but that the underlying problems are not. Specialised equipment has many valuable uses, but it does not encourage interchangeability.

Maintainability

This refers to the ease of maintenance, which has an effect both on the size of workforce required and the skills needed. What, indeed, are the maintenance requirements? This is primarily a matter for the manufacturer's specification, which itself should be based on the fleet reliability required by the customer. Not more than one failure per 10,000 miles is clearly less demanding than a maximum of one failure per 5,000 miles. How significant that is in terms of the amount of work to be done, the manpower needed, and when, is another matter. Good design is essential. Thus, a window held in by a pre-formed rubber moulding can be replaced in less than an hour. If it is part of the train structure and glued in place, a replacement may take two days. One of these is waiting for the adhesive to cure.

Another factor is the accessibility of the equipment, from the viewpoint of those maintaining it.

Extra attention takes extra time in which to do it. This may have effects on the availability of the fleet. As part of the equation, it is necessary to add in the time for routine maintenance needs and casualty maintenance. This latter refers to the replacement and/or repair of components in which defects occur.

In summary, this section on train specifications suggests that the operators need to make up their minds about what standards they are seeking and what is involved in ensuring that they are met. The resourcing required needs to match those standards and may, if desired, become the

Above: The 1995 tube stock features some tip-up seats, as seen here on the leading car of a northbound train at Golders Green, at about 08.30 on 21 March 2000. In recent times, Londoners have been favoured with copies of a free newspaper, *Metro*, which can be picked up at Underground stations. As this picture shows, several copies have been abandoned on the seats, and it is still early in the day. The clearance of rubbish from trains is a major task in terms of its sheer volume, which is not perhaps helped by copious quantities of free literature. *John Glover*

subject of an enforceable contract. This is not to suggest that standards should be merely imposed by the operator/customer; the subject is far too complex and worthwhile trade-offs may well exist. However, he who is uncertain as to what he wants is unlikely to be very satisfied with what he achieves.

The use of penalties for non-performance is now well established, as in the responsibility for delays to train services on the National Railways network. Other than trivial delays, all have to be attributed to the fault of either Railtrack or the train operating company. Penalties are exacted accordingly. Similar regimes may be applied to rolling stock performance, and the formulaic approach has many advantages. That way, everybody

knows where they stand, and the scope for major dissension is limited to that for major problems.

However, new rolling stock takes time to bed down. Teething troubles may be acceptable as long as they are addressed quickly. Does the manufacturer offer any form of guarantee? And, however carefully the manufacturer may specify the maintenance activities to be achieved, experience is still a hard master. Reliability and availability can be assessed accurately only over a period of time, and certainly not in less than a year. This may have implications for the staging of payments for new vehicles.

Types of Train

There are two basic types of train on the

Above: As this view shows, the matching up of the train's doors and the platform doors does not have to be exact. There is substantial eastbound traffic in this view taken at 09.05:42 on 20 March 2000 at Canada Water, to the extent that the lady on the platform has apparently decided to wait a couple of minutes for the next train. Seating space on the Jubilee Line stock is more limited than on any of the others presently in service on London Underground. *John Glover*

Underground system: the large surface stock and the tube stock. With the original cut-and-cover construction, the lines were built to what amounts to a constricted version of the full-size loading gauge. This results in surface vehicles with a body height of about 3,800mm above rail level. The tube stock, much more restricted, has a corresponding height of 2,870mm. This has an immediate effect in that while tube stock may, at least in theory, operate on surface lines, the reverse is clearly not generally true. Where both stocks run side by side and there are crossovers between the tracks, a secure method of ensuring that surface stock does not enter tube-gauge tunnels is necessary.

There are also differences in body widths. All tube stock is 2,640mm wide or thereabouts, but the width of surface stock is 2,850mm (D stock), 2,920mm (C stock) and 2,950mm (A stock). This is wider than any train on the National Railways network. On the few occasions where both tube and surface stock operate regularly on the same track, as for instance

at Acton Town and Ealing Common, the train-to-platform gap will vary. Here, D stock is 220mm wider than the 1973 Piccadilly Line trains, which means an increased stepping distance from the platform of 110mm (just over 4in).

However, this is not the only difference, the other being floor height above rail. The surface stock's height above rail is 980mm (3ft 3in); this compares with tube stock at 750mm (2ft 6in). Platforms thus have to be built to a compromise height to avoid a big step either up or down. Such problems may still be apparent when trains of different stocks run either side of an island platform. Although there is no physical inter-running, either the platform has to slope, or the track formation height has to be different. The latter is clearly more desirable, subject to the attentions of on-track engineering maintenance machinery.

Differing platform heights, to which may be added the effects of track and hence platform curvature on stepping distances, pose some awkward problems in respect of requirements for wheelchair

Top left: A train of refurbished 1973 stock arrives at North Ealing with a service for Rayners Lane on 20 March 2000. *John Glover*

Above: The D stock interiors consist mostly, but not entirely, of longitudinal seats. There are also a few single seats. These trains too have single doors. *John Glover*

Left: The 1983 tube stock was not a successful build; the single doors slowed access and took extra time to shut. It was used on the Jubilee Line until replaced by the 1996 stock. A train stands at Charing Cross station, now abandoned for regular use. *John Glover*

access. At least as importantly, less than desirable arrangements slow the boarding and alighting times of everybody.

The individual cars are semi-permanently coupled together into units of two, three or four cars. The cars are of various types, for instance the driving motor with cab and traction motors (DM), with automatic couplings at their outer ends, uncoupling non-driving motor car, which has traction equipment and at the end with an automatic coupling, a simple control panel to enable it to act as a driving position for shunting within depot limits (UNDM), and trailer (T),

with no traction control equipment. The combination of cars has to meet the operational requirements of the line. These include the ability to split trains into two self-contained units. The A stock sometimes operates as four-car units, although not all eight-car trains can be split for this purpose. On lines where the rolling stock can be turned in service, as on the Hainault Central Line loop, for instance, or on the Piccadilly at Heathrow or Northern at Kennington, it is useful if units can be double ended so that groups of cars can be coupled up whichever way they are facing.

Rolling Stock Types and Seat Densities Compared

Type	Company	Line	Cars/ train	Train length (m)	Total seats	Seats/ 100m	Notes
1996	LUL	Jubilee	6	107	200	188	
C	LUL	Circle, H&C, Edgware Rd/W'don	6	93	192	207	before/after refurbishment
1992	LUL	Central	8	130	272	209	
1973	LUL	Piccadilly	6	105	228	218	as refurbished
1995	LUL	Northern	6	107	248	233	includes 48 tip-up seats
1967	LUL	Victoria	8	128	304	237	
1973	LUL	Piccadilly	6	105	264	252	as built
1992	LUL	Bakerloo	7	112	268	238	
D	LUL	District	6	109	280	256	
A	LUL	Metropolitan	8	129	464	359	includes 16 tip-up seats
455	BR	South Western, South Central	8	159	636	400	
315	BR	Great Eastern	8	159	636	400	
465/466	BR	South Eastern	10	205	864	422	
4SUB	Southern	South Western, South Central	8	152	772	509	slam-door stock
Quint-Art	LNER	Great Eastern	10	133	888	668	slam-door stock
4DD	BR(S)	South Eastern	8	152	1,104	727	slam-door inc 88 tip-up

Perch seats are excluded from the calculations; these may be found in 1992 and 1996 stocks. Tip-up seats, where fitted, are counted as full seats.

Capacity Issues

Among the attributes for which the operator will look is the train capacity. Crudely, the more people that the train can carry, the more that asset can earn for the operating company. Whether or not capacity is fully used at all times is another matter; this section is concerned with the factors which determine capacity. As will be seen, this is a complex subject.

An Underground train has three key components when it comes to capacity, and these are discussed in turn. These components are:

1. The seats
2. The car length and train length
3. The doors.

Seats

It is axiomatic that people standing take up less floor space than do those who are seated. Thus, the fewer seats provided, the greater the carrying capacity of the car.

While this might perhaps lead logically to a conclusion that the most capacious vehicle would have no seats at all (and this has been tried in Tokyo), the reality is that under-seat space may be and is used to house all manner of equipment. It is also relatively accessible for maintenance purposes. This might be associated with the door operations or the running gear, but, critically, this includes arches for the wheels on tube stock. From the point of view of the present discussion, this also limits seating layout options.

It is a fair comment that busy services operating largely, if not entirely, within central London might need rather different interior configurations for the stock than those running perhaps 50km (30 miles) into the suburbs.

With seats, the crucial questions are:

- How many?
- Longitudinal or transverse, or a mixture?
- What dimensions (width and pitch)?

Above: The Victoria Line comes to the surface at Northumberland Park only, for depot access and not in public service. On 25 November 1998, a number of 1967 stock units are seen within the depot undergoing attention. *John Glover*

The table opposite shows the seating capacity and seating density of the various train types, and some comparisons with National Railways vehicles performing similar work.

Seats may be arranged longitudinally, as is becoming increasingly common, or transversely across the width of the vehicle. Any seating layout arrangement has to allow for passengers to enter or leave from the transverse seats next to the windows, which are thus not adjacent to a central gangway. Ideally, this should avoid those on the outside having to leave their seats while this takes place (as in a traditional bus seat type arrangement), but the minimum adjustment is likely to be having to move one's legs sideways.

The longitudinal arrangement creates no such difficulties, but this suffers from passengers' legs projecting, sometimes excessively, into the area to be used (nominally) by standing passengers. More general movements associated with boarding and alighting are impeded when this happens. This can be eased by good seat design.

Both arrangements have their advantages and disadvantages, but these are compounded by the allowances made by the car designer for seat width and seat pitch. People are getting larger. Press reports in recent times have suggested that in North America a seat width of 18in (460mm) is no longer considered sufficient, and that there may be a requirement to move to 20in or 21in (510mm or 530mm) to ensure passenger comfort. It will be interesting to see if similar developments take place in Britain;

Above: Differing floor heights of D surface and 1973 tube stock are very noticeable at Ealing Common, where both use the same platform. In this view of a D stock train, the single sliding door has begun to close. As can be seen, the floor height is well above the platform. *John Glover*

there are more visitors to London from the USA than from any other single country.

It is felt that the most meaningful comparison between stock types is the number of seats provided per unit length of train, taken as 100m. This eliminates the effects of the train lengths themselves varying, and concentrates more effectively on their internal layout. Thus, the 105m of a refurbished 1973 stock Piccadilly Line train now has 218 seats, compared with 252 beforehand. This is the result of eliminating some seats and replacing them with more luggage accommodation, plus some perch seats (which are not counted as seats for the present purpose). Notably, Piccadilly traffic includes much to and from Heathrow. Other recent stock has considerably fewer seats, with 188 only for the 1996 Jubilee Line stock. These all show the result of current thoughts on making seating longitudinal only to obviate the need for those on the inside of a transverse seat to push past to get out.

The Metropolitan main line A stock has a much higher seating capacity; this was maximised to compensate the good people of Amersham and the like for the loss of their compartment stock. The A stock has 3 + 2 seating each side of a gangway, and in this respect is more akin to the National Railways stock. Seating capacity on the latter is higher still, reaching a remarkable 668 per 100 metres on the London & North Eastern Railway Quint-Art (five-car articulated) sets which used to ply their way out of Liverpool Street in steam days. These remarkable vehicle sets were originally constructed with First, Second and Third Class compartments. Both the Second and Third Class were expected to carry 12 people seated in each compartment, but only 10 in the First Class. Subsequently, they were converted to Third and later Second Class throughout.

The table on page 48 shows clearly how seating densities can vary, but there is nothing to touch the old slam-door compartment stock (the Southern 4SUB units being another variety of this breed) if what was wanted was to seat the maximum numbers possible in the smallest possible space. However, the honours go to the only double-deck trains to run in Britain, the Bulleid 4DD stock which sported an amazing 1,104 seats in an eight-car train. Seating density in these was nearly four times as much as in the new 1996 Jubilee Line tube stock.

Generally, seats should be arranged so as to minimise the distance between each and the nearest door.

Train Length

Broadly speaking, train capacity is proportional to train length. This reflects the floor area available, and thus the number of seats which can be placed upon it. The longer the train, the more passengers that can be accommodated. The table opposite (*above right*) compares the train lengths of the various type of Underground stock with each other but

Rolling Stock Types and Train Lengths

Type	Company	Line	Average car length (m)	Cars/ train	Train length (m)
A	LUL	East London, Chesham branch	16.2	4	65
1992	LUL	Waterloo & City	16.2	4	65
C	LUL	Circle, H&C, Edgware Rd/W'don	15.5	6	93
1973	LUL	Piccadilly	17.4	6	105
1995	LUL	Northern	17.8	6	107
1996	LUL	Jubilee	17.8	6	107
D	LUL	District	18.2	6	109
1972	LUL	Bakerloo	16.1	7	112
1967	LUL	Victoria	16.1	8	128
A	LUL	Metropolitan	16.2	8	129
1992	LUL	Central	16.2	8	130
Quint-Art	LNER	Great Eastern	13.3	10	133
4SUB	SR	South Western, South Central	19.0	8	152
4DD	BR(S)	South Eastern	19.0	8	152
315	BR	Great Eastern	19.9	8	159
455	BR	South Western/South Central	19.9	8	159
465/466	BR	South Eastern	20.5	10	205
Mean values			17.4	7.1	124

also with a selection of the trains on the inner suburban services which are used, or in some cases have been used, on the National Railways system.

If, for the time being, we discard the short trains of A stock and the 1992 Waterloo & City Line tube stock, train lengths vary between that of the C stock at 93m, and the longest Underground train of 1992 stock at 130m. These are the eight-car trains used on the Central Line. However, adding in the National Railways trains, train length expands to 205m, which is that of the 10-car Class 465/466 Networker combinations operating out of Charing Cross and Cannon Street. This is well over twice the length of the C stock used on the Circle, Hammersmith & City and Edgware Road-Wimbledon lines.

It might well be asked why such differences occur. Even within the dedicated Underground fleets, the range for stock on the sub-surface lines varies from 129m for the A stock, which provides a joint service between Baker Street and Aldgate with the 93m C stock. On the south side of the Circle, eastwards to Upminster and south to Wimbledon, the puny C stock shares the service

provision with the 109m D stock. It is only west of Baker Street towards Hammersmith, and around the Circle towards Gloucester Road, plus short sections in the Aldgate area, that only the C stock may be found.

The simple answer is, of course, that platform lengths vary in different parts of the system for what may be quite complex historical reasons. Those on the west side of the Circle, at points such as Bayswater, are notoriously tight for length. Elsewhere, platform lengths may not really be adequate, as observation of A stock trains stopping at Great Portland Street will confirm. There are other tight points, such as the turnback central platform at Putney Bridge.

While the C stock, the first batch of which dates from 1969, was built to cope with the infrastructure limitations, it is perhaps surprising that platform lengthening has not been pursued more vigorously as an 'easy' way of increasing overall line capacity. It was designed with the thought that if platforms were lengthened, the trains could be coupled into eight-car lengths to operate the main District Line service.

As the table on page 51 shows, there is no magic about the length of an A stock train; indeed, the former British Rail operations include 12-car trains, but these do not provide what might be termed generically 'inner-suburban' services.

Given that all drivers need to draw trains up to what were once mirrors but are now ever more sophisticated devices for observing what is going on down the length of the platform, the train length variations are felt at the rear of the train. A C stock train is over two car lengths shorter than the eight-cars of A stock and one car shorter than the D stock. At the very least, this does not make for even train loading, since passengers will, if in doubt, position themselves where they know they can board the approaching train directly.

Exactly the same arguments can be applied to the tube lines; differences range from 105m for six-cars on the Piccadilly to 130m for eight-cars on the Central. Here the odd man out is the Waterloo & City Line, with the platforms at Bank dictating a limit of four-car and hence 65m trains. Platform lengthening is not easy work, let it be said, but it was carried out successfully on the original Central Line route from Wood Lane to Liverpool Street in the late 1930s. The results can be seen today, particularly at the 'original' stations like Lancaster Gate with their white tiling. The 'hump' on which each station was constructed, to aid retardation for arriving trains and also to allow them to accelerate away faster, is now partially incorporated within the platform area.

Of the other tube lines, only the Victoria Line (opened 1968-72) has platforms of commensurate length, although the Jubilee Line extension has been built with a view to adding another (seventh) car to the trains when traffic warrants it. This approach was adopted also for the deep-level Tyne & Wear Metro stations (opened from 1980).

Finally, it may also be noted from the table that car lengths vary. In favour of longer cars is the reduction in the space lost to passenger accommodation at the car ends; if seven-car trains are replaced by six longer cars, as happened on the re-equipment of the Northern Line, there is clearly a net gain in passenger space. Capital and maintenance costs are also likely to be lower, as there is one set less of running gear, which includes the car bogies.

On the other hand, longer cars mean wider platform-to-train gaps on curves. The problem occurs at the car ends when the platform is on the inside of the curve, and at the middle when it is on the outside. This is a substantial disadvantage, especially at busy stations where quite extreme cases occur. Some of the worst are at Bank, Central Line (both platforms) and at Embankment (Northern Line, northbound only). The result is a slowing down of alighting and joining times, leading to longer station stops. There is also an increased accident risk. In addition, car width decreases as length increases. This is the reason for D stock being narrower than C stock.

One possible compromise is the use of articulated sets of vehicles. Articulation reduces the overall weight, since each pair of carriage ends is carried on a single bogie rather than two. There is no buffing or drawgear equipment needed intermediately within the set. Articulation may improve riding qualities (although this is not likely to be a problem). It was practised extensively by H. N. Gresley, the Carriage & Wagon Superintendent of the Great Northern Railway, between 1905 and 1911. Shorter vehicle bodies also become a practicable proposition, which can obviate some of the difficulties outlined above. For suburban work, these included the Quint-Art (short for five-car articulated) sets of slam-door stock included in the tables and referred to again later. Present ideas for the articulation of new trains use sliding-door stock.

Doors

Space not occupied by seats can be used by those standing; as a seated person takes up more floor space that one who stands, fewer seats usually means a greater overall train capacity. But it also means more space for doors.

The sliding doors, or similar types such as plug doors, are here to stay. With doors, a similar series of questions can be asked:

- How many?
- Single-leaf or double-leaf?
- Where on the body side should they be positioned?
- How wide should each door be?

The table below shows the present situation. The double-leaf door is found most frequently; on National Railways trains it is invariably positioned at a third and two-thirds of the way along the bodyside. Many Underground cars have the same arrangement, but on a conventional tube car, the wheels protruding through the floor prevent the provision of double doorways evenly spaced along the side of the car. Hence, it is usual on the Underground for a single door to be placed at the car ends, unless that end has a driver's cab. A door in this position allows passengers to exit from a crowded train, minimising the risk of

Rolling Stock Types and Door Configurations Compared

Type	Company	Line	Cars/ train no	Train length (m)	Single doors no	Door width (m)	Total door width (m)	Doors as % of length
455	BR	South Western	8	159	32	0.49	15.68	9.8
465/466	BR	South Eastern	10	205	40	0.65	26.00	12.7
315	BR	Great Eastern	8	159	32	0.65	20.80	13.1
4DD	BR(S)	South Eastern	8	152	48	0.60	28.8	18.9
1973	LUL	Piccadilly	6	105	34	0.69	23.32	22.3
1995/96	LUL	Northern and Jubilee	6	107	34	0.71	24.14	22.6
1967	LUL	Victoria	8	128	44	0.69	30.18	23.5
A	LUL	Metropolitan	8	129	44	0.69	30.18	23.4
D	LUL	District	6	109	24	1.07	25.68	23.5
1972	LUL	Bakerloo	7	112	39	0.69	26.75	23.8
4SUB	Southern	South Western, South Central	8	152	72	0.60	43.20	28.5
1992	LUL	Central	8	130	46	0.83	38.27	29.4
Quint-Art	LNER	Great Eastern	10	133	74	0.60	44.40	33.4
C	LUL	Circle, H&C, Edgware Rd/W'don	6	93	48	0.69	32.93	35.5

Single doors are defined as the number of door leaves on each side available for public use.
Underground D stock has single-leaf doors only, and the C stock double doors only.
Other Underground stocks have a mixture of single and double doors.
National Railways trains of the sliding door variety have double doors throughout.
4SUB, 4DD and Quint-Art stock all had slam doors only.

being trapped by too many standing passengers. Whatever the door arrangement, the provision of 'stand back' space to keep standing passengers clear of the doors is now generally recognised.

With slam doors of a nominal 600mm, only one person can enter, or leave, at any one time; with wide double doors such as the 2 x 830mm doors of the 1992 stock, certainly two may make a move simultaneously. With narrower versions, the ability for two movements at once is less certain; amongst other things, it depends upon crowds on platforms, and the ability to actually get off the train. It was considered that the most meaningful measurement of door space, again, was the total width of doors available in a 100m length of train.

The number of doors to be provided on the side of each vehicle depends upon the volume of on/off movements, which are likely to be high on virtually all London Underground operations. They may reasonably be expected to be lower on National Railways' services.

With most Underground stock, door space takes up around 23% of the total length, give or take a bit. The main exception is the C stock, whose four pairs of double doors on each side of each car offer no less than 35% of the total length as door space. Such arrangements are ideal for shifting crowds, especially for short-distance travel where the ability to secure a seat is of little importance. At the other end of the scale, the National Railways trains have much less door space, the minimum being that of the Class 455 units now used by South West Trains and Connex SouthCentral. These have slightly less than 10% of the space available for doors, which themselves are the narrowest recorded.

This section would not be complete without a reference to the Quint-Art sets

Ⅱ *Below:* D stock trains are lined up in Ealing Common depot on 6 February 2000. *John Glover*

and 4SUB units. It will be seen that these managed to combine high seating capacity (see page 48) with large numbers of doors for quick entry/exit (see page 54). They did the job they were designed to do very well. But compartment sets are not everybody's favourite, and slam doors are most unlikely to be seen again, especially on the Underground.

The author hopes that this section has explored some of the trade-offs in the train length, number of seats and number of doors debate. He has not attempted to cover the issues of standing space in any detail; another relevant aspect here is trying to persuade people not to stand where they obstruct the doors and impede others. Unfortunately, this tends also to be the most comfortable place to stand.

Standing Passengers

As to how many can stand in a train, such calculations are needed for two reasons. There is the technical one in which the absolute maximum are assumed to be present, so that acceleration and braking rates can be calculated, and also the adequacy of the suspension. When it comes to actual behaviour, counts undertaken by the author suggest that the effective capacity is likely to be all seats taken, plus around 25 in each double-door area, 15 in a single-door area, and eight along the centre gangway between sets of doors. Thus on a standard tube car, such as a Victoria Line 1967 stock 36-seat trailer, this would equate to $15+8+25+8+25+8+15$, or 104 standing, and a total load of 140. It is not so much that more cannot get on; rather that they choose not to do so. This is in respect of each car, but allowance must be made for different levels of demand at different points on the train. Overall, this might equate to an effective maximum of around 1,000 people on an eight-car Victoria Line train at any one time.

Although there is more headroom in surface stock than on the tube stock, the floor area is not significantly different.

Similar calculations can be made for these trains.

What, however, constitutes a crush load? Readers may be interested in the congestion indices used by Tokyo operator, JR-East:

- **100%** All seats taken with some standing passengers holding straps or door posts.
- **150%** Shoulders touch, but it is possible to read a newspaper easily.
- **180%** Bodies start to touch, but it is still just possible to read a newspaper.
- **200%** Bodies touch firmly, pressure being felt, it is possible to read a small book or magazine.
- **250%** Everyone leans in unison as the train moves, passengers cannot move their bodies or even their hands.

The foregoing shows again that there are no easy answers. For Underground use, what might constitute an ideal train? This would have double-doorways evenly spaced throughout its length, no gaps between cars, short car bodies (enabling width to be maximised and minimising the gap at current platforms) and a flat floor. Considerable work has been undertaken in recent years to confirm that such a train is technically feasible. The only 'engineering' problem is with a tube version, where the small space between floor and track would constrain wheel diameters to less than 500mm and require very compact traction equipment.

Depots

An important requirement is the provision of depot accommodation for the fleet, where repairs and day-to-day maintenance can be undertaken. Normally, this will be close to the line's main stabling accommodation.

Depot size is dependent upon fleet size, plus some spare for non-revenue-earning vehicles such as those for engineering purposes. Depots need covered accommodation with access pits, and the ability to lift cars off their bogies. An

overhead crane, if not an absolute necessity, is a valuable alternative to jacking. Routine maintenance work and component changing needs to take place, which means that a component stores supply must be available. Stabling sidings can be covered, and this provides extra security; it also offers cold weather protection.

Depot layout should be such that trains either leaving it for service or entering it after being taken out of service can be routed via the train washer. This ensures that external washes are performed at least daily. Internal cleaning and sweeping out the cars can be undertaken in the stabling sidings. Double-ended depot layouts allow any derailment or other mishap to be circumnavigated, but the space available may not allow for such niceties. Even so, track layouts which give some flexibility have an edge over other designs.

Depending on the line length, depot facilities may be towards one or other ends of the line, or both. More than one depot makes it easier and faster for trains to be deployed near the points at which they are wanted, rather than to have to travel for perhaps 45min before they reach that point. It is not realistic to

think in terms of depots in central London, as land prices alone would rule this out. This did not stop the Great Western Railway from buying an extremely expensive piece of land on which to build Hammersmith depot, much to the annoyance of the Metropolitan Railway. For planning purposes, an area of about 250sq m per car is needed, so a depot for 25 trains will take up a considerable area.

The principal depots, by line, are (*below*):

Bakerloo	Stonebridge Park
Central	West Ruislip, Hainault and White City
District	Ealing Common and Upminster
East London	New Cross
Hammersmith & City/Circle	Hammersmith
Jubilee	Stratford Market and Neasden
Metropolitan	Neasden
Northern	Golders Green and Morden
Piccadilly	Northfields and Cockfosters
Victoria	Northumberland Park
Waterloo & City	Waterloo

5

Timetable Compilation

On the face of it, timetable compilation is quite simple. The passengers who can be moved are a function of train capacity and the service interval (*below*):

Data on the capability of the infrastructure, and of the details of train performance, can then be combined in the construction of the timetable. This can go

$$\text{Passengers per minute} = \frac{\text{Train capacity (at reasonable comfort levels)}}{\text{Interval in minutes}}$$

Below: The platform width at Canary Wharf Jubilee Line station is huge, as can be seen by the size of the banks of escalators. Even the roundels bearing the station name are larger than usual, as can be judged by the lady sitting on the seat nearest the camera. This photograph was taken on 20 March 2000 during a short gap between trains; in a few moments the platforms will be flooded with people. *John Glover*

Above: Timetable compilation is always easier when there is plenty of infrastructure. This picture, taken on 6 February 2000, shows a 1973 stock Piccadilly Line train approaching Acton Town with an eastbound service. Essentially, this is only a two-way junction, the alternative destinations looking in this direction being Heathrow (lower level) and Ealing Broadway/Rayners Lane (upper level). There is also access to Ealing Common depot in the background, right. *John Glover*

through several iterations until a satisfactory result is obtained. It is then possible to construct train and train crew diagrams. Real life, however, isn't quite as simple!

For a start, demand varies according to the time of day and the day of the week. The differing requirements are illustrated by an off-peak/peak comparison:

- Off peak. Service patterns must be selected for repeating operations over periods lasting several hours. The patterns must provide a reasonable match to train frequencies required. If there are branches and/or intermediate reversing points, the service pattern will comprise two or more elements, which may or may not be self-contained. For elements to be self-contained the round-trip-time (rtt), including layovers

at both ends, must be an exact multiple of the service interval for that element (the Circle Line is a special case with 48-60min rtt). The layovers at the ends of the branches and at intermediate reversing points must relate to one another in a way determined by the respective running times so that the services mesh correctly in the return direction. Last, but not least, conflicts at flat junctions, including approaches to termini, must be avoided. The merits and demerits of self-contained services need to be considered.

- Peak. The peak service will not repeat itself as a pattern, and the service in one direction need not match that in the other direction, either in frequency or timing. The aim must be to get the best match at each point to the frequency

Above: At Green Park, the Piccadilly Line platforms are largely in original style. The 'suicide pit' can be seen beneath the return current rail in the centre of the picture. Platform width reduces towards the platform ends, where this view was taken on 20 March 2000. *John Glover*

required, always having regard to the train resources available, the locations where they can be brought into service and taken out of service, and capacity limitations, including the consequences of extended station dwells. There may be a preponderance of trains in one direction in the morning peak and in the opposite direction in the evening peak, provided that suitably placed berthing for midday stabling is available.

The Underground's train planners are stretched in all directions. They are expected to produce timetables and schedules which meet a large number of often conflicting needs. The timetable is the practical expression of the operational requirements of the business. These are specified in a fully workable form that also commits a certain level of resources in order for the timetable to be fulfilled. It is the consolidated result of the objectives

and constraints in the following main areas:

- commercial aspirations;
- infrastructure capabilities and signalling headways;
- train performance and running times;
- resource availability, both equipment and manpower;
- service volumes;
- customer volumes and demand;
- proof against random disturbances to operations, and
- economy in resource allocation.

Having achieved this for the basic plan, the timetable planners must immediately do it all over again for the changes caused by Saturdays, Sundays, engineering work, sports fixtures, staff absence, equipment failures or totally unforeseen circumstances. Operators must calculate point-to-point journey times quickly and

Above: The availability of a south to north crossover at Piccadilly Circus, Bakerloo Line, allows trains from Queen's Park to be turned back, but only the one platform is available. In days past there was a scissors crossover, which would have made the layout much more flexible. A northbound train of 1972 stock is arriving in March 1995. *John Glover*

accurately, to ensure that the working timetable is up to date and is consistent with resources of both crews and equipment.

Above all, they need to get it right, with no errors, and in a tightly controlled time-scale.

Commercial Aspirations

The business needs to specify what the production managers should be trying to achieve. On a system such as the Underground, this might be taken as the level of service on each of the well-known lines. However, even with lines which are physically self-contained such as the Victoria Line between Brixton and Walthamstow Central, there are several options.

- Is the service frequency requirement the same for all parts of the line? If so, this means all trains should run between the

end points of the line at all times, and there is no benefit in terminating certain trains at (for instance) Seven Sisters (northbound) or Victoria (southbound).

- How much capacity in terms of seat/km (or more realistically place/km) should be provided? To what extent does the capacity required vary at different times of the day or week? Is there a directional flow, as in bringing commuter traffic to central London in the mornings? Might there be any seasonal element? What should be done at public and bank holidays? London buses have special 'school holiday' timetables on many busy routes, while the Paris Metro thins out the peak hour service in the summer.

- Moving into more problematical areas, when should the first and last services be run? The times of these have been remarkably constant over many years, but social change is continuous. Recent years have seen a considerable loosening of

Above: Underground colour light signals are seen at Shoreditch, the single track terminus, on 13 March 1999. The track becomes double almost immediately beyond the platform end. This section of line will be abandoned when the extension to the old Broad Street formation is built. *John Glover*

regulation. This has included the hours during which people may work, the times at which shops can open, the relaxation of licensing laws and the general effects of a more pluralistic society. How should the Underground respond?

It is matters of this nature that have to be defined; timetable compilation aims to provide for these requirements as precisely as possible.

A further complication is the compilation of crew duty rosters to match the timetable. These need to take into account the need for rest periods, to ensure that train crew end up back at their home depot, and to ensure that train crew are being used productively for as much of their shifts as possible. All has to be carried out within the terms of such management/staff agreements as exist, as well as making provision for annual leave, training and safety considerations.

Infrastructure Capabilities

Without infrastructure, there can be no service. There are perhaps two elements here. One is the provision of the track and signalling available for running services, the other is the need for its maintenance, renewal and updating.

Most of the Underground network consists of twin tracks with a limited number of crossover connections between them. Stations comprise either side or island platforms; the latter, if in tube tunnel sections, are effectively two tunnels side by side with connecting passageways between them. Some stations may feature a third platform, as for instance at Leytonstone, Central Line, where separate westbound platforms are available for trains arriving from Hainault and those from Woodford. This helps regulate out-of-course running, without leaving trains stranded while awaiting platform availability. A third platform is also useful if trains are to be terminated at an intermediate point, for example at North Greenwich on the Jubilee Line or Mansion House on the District. At other locations, though, trains may have to proceed to a siding (or sidings) beyond the platform and reverse there. This happens at Harrow & Wealdstone (Bakerloo Line, but on Railtrack property) and at West Hampstead (Jubilee Line).

More difficult is reversing in a single platform and returning direct. This can be practised at Piccadilly Circus, Bakerloo

Line, for trains arriving from the north, and was in continuous use during the long-term closure for repairs of the tunnel section beneath the Thames. Using one platform only for such a task, because that is all there is available, can seriously affect train frequencies. Most problematical of all is using a straight tunnel crossover, where the driver has to walk back through the train to reach the other cab.

For instance, when the Jubilee Line extension services were running between Stratford and Waterloo only and reversing there, this presented some crewing problems. During pre-service running, stepping back was practised. Using this method, the driver who brought a westbound train from Stratford into Waterloo picked up a second driver in

what was then the rear cab. The first driver took the train into the tunnel and stopped. He then shut down and the other opened up for the return journey. The first driver detrained at Waterloo on the eastbound platform and then made his way to the rear of the westbound platform, where the sequence would be repeated for the next train. This meant also that the first train could depart for Stratford while he was still walking to his next cab at the far end.

However, this proved too inflexible, especially if trains were running out of sequence or late. When passenger services began, the driver who brought the first train in detrained. Two crew, one in each cab, then took it forwards into the tunnel for reversal. One shut down,

Below: Amersham station is laid out in spacious style. A train of A stock approaches from the sidings, ready to form a train to Aldgate on 14 November 1998. *John Glover*

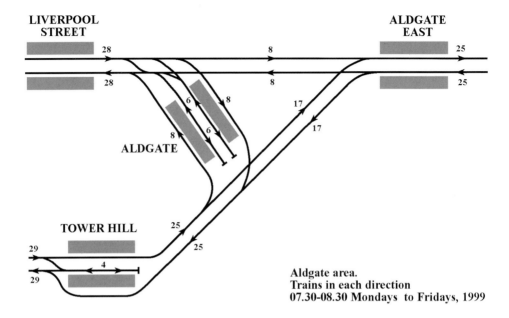

Aldgate area.
Trains in each direction
07.30-08.30 Mondays to Fridays, 1999

the other opened up, and the train arrived back in the eastbound platform as before. Although it required an additional driver, this proved much more satisfactory, given also that capacity was limited to a maximum of 15 trains per hour.

What can, or cannot, be achieved is dependent not only upon the availability of crossovers and other track features but also upon the capabilities of the signalling and other safety systems.

Junction conflicts can also be a serious cause of delays. In the Aldgate area, there is a triangle of three flat junctions, with huge scope for conflicting movements. Without wishing to sound defeatist, it is quite unusual to be able to pass through this area on a train without at least a small delay. The complexity is perhaps evident from the diagram, with a high number of potential conflicts in almost any movement made. If service frequencies are relatively high, and the numbers of trains over each leg are as shown for the busiest 60min period in the morning peak hour, such

arrangements are potent sources of problems.

It is of course possible to make more than one move at once, such as in both directions on the District Line or the Circle Line, and such opportunities need to be used. However, this is not the only set of junctions encountered, and 'getting it right' in the Aldgate area may present further difficulties around Earl's Court. The goal is the best result overall.

The train services represented are as follows:

- 8tph Hammersmith & City Line services between Liverpool Street and Aldgate East, both directions
- 8tph Circle Line services, Liverpool Street-Aldgate-Tower Hill, both directions
- 12tph Metropolitan Line services Liverpool Street to centre platforms at Aldgate, both directions
- 17tph District Line trains between Tower Hill and Aldgate East, both directions
- 4tph District Line trains from the west to

Tower Hill, terminating there and
returning

That such a service is possible at all on the
flat junctions as shown is quite
remarkable. Whether it really makes the
best use possible of the infrastructure is
another matter, and possible opportunities
are discussed later.

Signalling

The frequency of service to be provided is
constrained also by the signalling, which
affects the minimum achievable headway
between trains. This ranges from 24tph
upwards, according to line.

Basic Underground signalling is
two-aspect colour lights. There is an
intermittent automatic train protection
system, by means of train stops at each
signal. The arm of the train stop is raised
when the signal is at danger. Every train
has a tripcock attached to the leading
bogie, which is operated by a raised train
stop arm and applies the emergency brake.

Trains are kept separated from each
other by the sections of line which each
signal controls, each being exclusive to
their own use, plus a safety overlap
distance beyond. Thus, for a signal to clear
and for it to be safe for a train to enter
that section, the preceding train must have
left the one next ahead. Signal spacing can
be closed up by inserting additional
signals, and thus shortening the individual
sections. This allows trains to follow each
other more closely, as described previously.

The capacity of a signalling system is
related to the headway. This is defined as
the minimum time between two successive
trains, each travelling at maximum speed,
which includes an allowance for the
platform dwell time in station areas. This
allowance can become inadequate if
station dwell times increase, as they may
do if the levels of passenger traffic grow,
and this increases the minimum headway
attainable. If trains travel more slowly due
to increased loads, the result is similar.
The conventional signalling systems have

no real means of addressing this, other
than a repositioning of the signals and
increasing their total numbers. By
definition, such action is costly and cannot
be implemented quickly.

The Victoria Line has automatic
protection by means of coded track
circuits, which are detected by the train as
follows:

- 420 pulses per minute allows a train to
  start and run at maximum speed;
- 270 pulses per minute allows a train to
  restart after a signal stop and permits
  motoring at up to 25mph;
- 180 pulses per minute is used to stop
  trains approaching a signal and allows
  train speeds up to 25mph, but does not
  allow motoring.

One of these three codes must be
present before a train can be driven
automatically (or in coded manual). If
25mph is exceeded in 270 or 180 codes,
the automatic brake will be applied.

A 120 code is used only by the
signalling equipment to test whether track
circuits are occupied. Trains cannot detect
it. This is complemented by a separate
automatic train operation system (ATO),
which drives the train between stations.
All the operator has to do is to operate the
doors and press a pair of buttons in the
cab to start the train. A limitation of the
Victoria Line arrangements is that trains
cannot be driven manually at full speed as
there is no advance warning in the cab of
a change in safety code.

The Central Line has a more complex
automatic train protection system, which
warns drivers in advance of changes in the
maximum safe speed and overcomes this
problem. This is now being
complemented by an automatic train
operation system.

Train Performance and
Running Times

There is no problem nowadays in
providing adequate accelerating and

Above: The kiosk at Finchley Road on the southbound platform is perhaps a useful service to passengers, but such obstructions do not help those rushing from Metropolitan to Jubilee trains, or vice versa. The date is 20 March 2000. *John Glover*

braking powers on a train; rather, these have to be controlled in order to stop passengers, especially those standing, from being thrown all over the place. Other than for an emergency stop, the aim is to limit such forces in the interests of passenger comfort.

Tests have shown that a combination of both acceleration and the rate of change in acceleration determine passenger comfort levels. The comfort limit for acceleration is generally accepted as being between 4.8km/h/sec² (3mph/sec²) and 6.5km/h/sec² (4mph/sec²), with a preference towards the lower end. The limit for rate of change of acceleration is taken as 2.75m/sec² (9ft/sec²). The provision for deceleration is similar, subject to an emergency deceleration rate of 6.5km/h/sec² (4mph/sec²). These rates were established in the USA in 1932, and corresponded broadly to the rates obtained by the then well-known and commonly found PCC streetcar.

Another factor which will affect overall running times is the time spent at stations. The Underground's Working Timetables include allowances for station dwell times. On the District Line, for instance, the standard off peak and weekend dwell time is 15sec, which is increased to 20sec for all stations between Earl's Court and Tower Hill, and also at the busier stations outside this area of Whitechapel, Mile End and Hammersmith. During the peaks, the 15sec stops become 20sec, and the 20sec stops 30sec. This has the effect of extending the time for a train to run from Upminster to Ealing Broadway from 79½min to 88min.

Much the same happens on other lines and differential stop times sometimes apply according to the peak direction. Thus the southbound trains in the morning peak of both the Metropolitan and Jubilee lines are allowed 40sec at Finchley Road, but only 30sec northbound. There is substantial

Above: The flyovers constructed at Barking in the late 1950s were part of an ambitious scheme to separate completely the Underground from the then British Railways operations. This meant that the trains of one could no longer affect the running of the other. A D stock train leaves for central London on 28 October 1998. *John Glover*

interchange between trains here, plus some obstructions on the island platform to negotiate! In the evenings both are allowed 30sec in each direction.

Weather can affect the condition of rails, the operation of equipment and general visibility. Train performance can suffer accordingly. While this is mainly an open-air problem, it affects all lines other than the Victoria and the Waterloo & City — and the Victoria Line trains still have to access Northumberland Park depot. The hazards are as follows:

- Sun — rails expand, driver visibility problems
- Fog — visibility problems
- Snow — blocks track, wheel slip, visibility problems
- Rain — floods track, affects track circuits
- Thunderstorms — electrical disturbances, can affect signalling

- Leaves — coat rails, affect track circuit continuity
- Ice — rails contract, affects third/fourth rail contact, icicles form in tunnels, water supplies and points freeze

The armoury against cold weather starts with point heaters. On each line a proportion of trains is equipped to spray de-icing fluid on the conductor rails during normal operation. They also have 'sleet brushes' which assist in scraping ice and snow off the conductor rails. When it is exceptionally cold or snow is forecast, trains are kept running through the night to keep the conductor rails clear. It is at such times that the apparently generous proportions of trains stabled under cover on the Underground proves very useful. Clearances are such that it is unacceptable for trains on many sections to enter service with more than a thin layer of snow on the roof.

Above: Keeping apart the surface and tube stocks is an absolute necessity when a tube tunnel looms up ahead. This is the defence at the approach to the Jubilee Line southbound platform at Finchley Road, seen here on 20 March 2000 with a 1996 stock train approaching. There is plenty of room below the gantry, but an A stock train would collide with the suspended phials and set off procedures aimed at stopping it very quickly. *John Glover*

The leaf fall season is a particular hazard on the Metropolitan main line, where special timetables are in force with additional running time allowed. This is with the objective of limiting acceleration and braking rates, thus avoiding wheel slip and the consequential damage to both wheels and rails. Despite selective tree felling and the laying of Sandite paste on the rails, the leaf mulch significantly extends emergency braking distances. To

overcome this, a 40mph speed restriction is imposed down the hill from Amersham to Rickmansworth. Leaf fall affects both trains and infrastructure; the lack of experience of some younger drivers leads them to be overcautious. Some need more help in judging the situation.

Another performance matter is the adequacy of the power supplies; if too many trains are accelerating simultaneously, there may be some problems here.

None of this, of course, prevents the timetable planners from getting it wrong, sometimes embarrassingly so. Major engineering work closed the short section of the Circle Line between High Street Kensington and Gloucester Road for nine weeks during 1998. Said the leaflet titled 'An Apology', rather plaintively, 'we had undertaken months of detailed planning (but) despite this our best efforts did not succeed. Small delays quickly built up to major disruption, not just on the Circle Line but also on the other lines which share the same track.' This was perhaps a case of being a little too optimistic as to what could be achieved with the resources available. Some judicious slack is always desirable, so that localised problems do not multiply into ones affecting a larger network. For those who have not experienced it, this can happen disconcertingly quickly.

Resource Availability
To run a service requires both a train and a driver; the last appearance of a guard on London Underground in normal passenger service was on the final run of the 1959 tube stock on the Northern Line on 27 January 2000. Guards had been eliminated progressively from 1984; the introduction of one-person operation was complete on the sub-surface lines by 1986 and on parts of the tube network by 1989. Guards on the Central, Northern and Waterloo & City lines were retained for up to another decade until the previous rolling stock was replaced with

new build. All passenger trains are now one-person operated. This, of course, includes the Victoria Line, which has never used guards.

Both train and crew have to be in the right place, at the right time, every time. This has to be related to depot locations and stabling points, and also to the main flows of traffic. Running a comprehensive service against the peak flows may seem unproductive, but the trains have to go one way in order that they can come back again.

The resources required to run the timetabled service vary considerably according to time of day and day of the week. The diagram below shows the train resource requirements in some detail:

Total trains in service by line, by type, by day of week and time of day.
As at 30 January 2000

Line	Car type	Mondays to Fridays				Saturdays		
		am	noon	pm	eve	am	noon	eve
Bakerloo	1972	32	26	32	21	20	26	21
Central	1992	72	45	72	30	32	45	30
Circle	C	14	14	14	14	10	14	14
District Edg Rd-W'don	C	8	8	10	8	6	8	8
District main	D	66	50	66	35	30	50	34
East London	A (4)	5	4	5	3	5	5	4
Hammersmith & City	C	17	14	15	16	8	14	14
Jubilee	1996	46	42	42	35	26	40	35
Metropolitan Amersham	A (8)	12	9	12	5	5	9	5
Metropolitan Chesham	A (4)	1	1	1	1	1	1	1
Metropolitan Uxbridge	A (8)	16	12	17	7	9	12	7
Metropolitan Watford	A (8)	15	8	14	6	7	8	5
Northern	1995	84	60	84	46	51	60	46
Piccadilly	1973	76	68	76	53	54	69	53
Victoria	1967	37	25	37	25	25	25	25
Waterloo & City	1992	4	3	4	2	2	2	2
Total trains in use		505	389	501	307	291	388	304
Total cars in use		3,346	2,542	3,322	1,997	1,918	2,536	1,975
Cars as % of maximum		100.0	76.0	99.3	59.7	57.3	75.8	59.0

Line	Car type	Sundays		
		am	noon	eve
Bakerloo	1972	11	26	21
Central	1992	21	38	28
Circle	C	10	14	14
District Edg Rd-W'don	C	4	8	8
District main	D	27	47	33
East London	A (4)	5	5	4
Hammersmith & City	C	8	11	11
Jubilee	1996	34	40	35
Metropolitan Amersham	A (8)	5	9	5
Metropolitan Chesham	A (4)	1	1	1
Metropolitan Uxbridge	A (8)	6	9	7
Metropolitan Watford	A (8)	7	11	5
Northern	1995	46	55	46
Piccadilly	1973	47	68	53
Victoria	1967	25	25	25
Waterloo & City	1992	0	0	0
Total trains in use		257	367	296
Total cars in use		1,669	2,345	1,925
Cars as % of maximum		49.9	70.1	57.5

TOWER HILL		MANSION HOUSE
STOPS HERE		PLAISTOW
		DAGENHAM EAST
→ BARKING		UPMINSTER
HIGH ST. KENSINGTON AND EDGWARE ROAD		HIGH ST. KENSINGTON

For Notting Hill Gate and Paddington take an Edgware Road train

Platform 1

Above: Telling passengers which train is which is not always easy; at Earl's Court the old boards are still in use — and they work. However, there is no means of telling what other trains are in the offing. This is the display on the eastbound platform on 15 June 1999. *John Glover*

It will be seen that the resources needed vary enormously. The number of trains needed for Saturday services in the middle of the day mirrors that of Mondays to Fridays, as do the evening services. Sunday services need fewer trains in the earlier parts of the day, but the evenings are again similar. On some lines, notably the Circle, the resource requirement varies but little; only the Waterloo & City has no service whatsoever on Sundays.

The number of trains is converted into the number of cars at the bottom of the table. It may be of interest that the average number of cars per train is now approximately 6.5. The only seven-car trains left are those on the Bakerloo, and the 1995/6 stocks are both six-car trains. Eight-car operation is confined to the Metropolitan, Central and Victoria lines.

Taking the maximum of 3,346 cars in use during the Monday to Friday morning peak as 100%, this drops to a low of 1,669 cars or a fraction under 50% on Sunday mornings. Car usage rises to 70% by midday. Throughout the week, evening car usage is running at about 60% of the peak maximum.

The usage figures do not refer to the whole fleet; the Annual Report for 1999/2000 records 3,954 cars as being in stock at the end of that year. This appears to be a substantial surplus, even allowing for cars undergoing overhaul, major maintenance or stopped for other reasons. However, the spare element was swelled by the stock replacement then under way on both the Jubilee and Northern lines. There are also substantial numbers of 1972 Mk I stock retained for possible refurbishment and reuse, plus the 16½ trains of 1983 stock, formerly on the Jubilee Line, earmarked to boost the Piccadilly Line fleet.

Service Volumes

The most appropriate of measures as to how much service is actually provided is the total train kilometres run in passenger service. This reflects not only the service intensity but also the length of the line.

The table below presents this information in terms of the total train km run per week on each line, broken down by day. Very nearly half the total train km are undertaken by the top three: the Piccadilly, the Northern and the District lines. All run intensive services over long stretches of the network. It is perhaps surprising that the services on the Metropolitan's long main line do not take that line higher, but service frequencies are lower.

At the other end of the scale, the Waterloo & City is shown to be a very limited operation. It is intensively used during the peaks on Mondays to Fridays, but much less so at other times. The City has little traffic outside working hours. Also in the modest category of service provision is the East London Line. Measures such as train km provided are of course reflected in the length of the line; it takes far more trains to run at a given headway on the Central Line than it would on either of these.

The total train km per week show less variation than might be expected, with Sunday service provision approaching three-quarters of that offered during the week. The calculation showing annual train km run makes assumptions, as specified, on the type of service operated on public and bank holidays, etc.

Customer Volumes

When do people want to travel? The annual station entry counts of London Underground give an indication of the usage of each station, which is also useful for spotting trends.

Total train km in passenger service by line and by day of week.
As at 30 January 2000

Line	Car type	Mon-Fri	Mon-Fri wk x 5	Sat	Sun	Weekly total	% total train km
Piccadilly	1973	36,650	183,249	33,533	29,243	246,025	19.0
Northern	1995	31,936	159,679	26,964	21,107	207,750	16.1
District	C/D	27,714	138,570	23,678	20,451	182,699	14.1
Jubilee	1996	22,566	112,830	20,877	18,155	151,862	11.7
Metropolitan	A	19,231	96,156	15,786	12,812	124,754	9.7
Central	1992	17,331	86,656	13,111	11,341	111,108	8.6
Victoria	1967	15,560	77,800	12,658	10,921	101,379	7.8
H&C/Circle	C	11,532	57,661	10,531	8,741	76,934	6.0
Bakerloo	1972	10,695	53,476	9,652	8,112	71,241	5.5
East London	A	2,033	10,165	1,845	1,517	13,527	1.0
Waterloo & City	1992	979	4,894	303	0	5,196	0.4
Total train km/wk		196,227	981,136	168,939	142,401	1,292,475	100.0
% operated by day		15.2	75.9	13.1	11.0	100.0	
Annual train km, millions			49.6	8.8	7.4	65.8	

Notes
Above calculations based on LUL figures and the daily/weekly figures have been rounded up/down where appropriate.
The East London service assumes Shoreditch operation.
The annual calculation assumes Monday to Friday services 253 days/yr, Saturdays 52 days/yr, Sundays 59 days/yr, and no service Christmas Day.

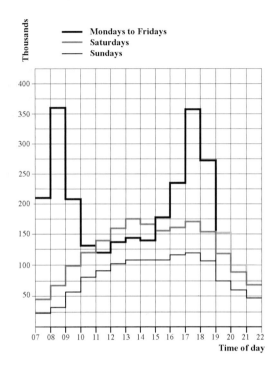

London Underground station entry counts, by hour, autumn 1998

Thousands

— Mondays to Fridays
— Saturdays
— Sundays

400
350
300
250
200
150
100
50

07 08 09 10 11 12 13 14 15 16 17 18 19 20 21 22

Time of day

The graph above is the summation of all the station entry counts on Mondays to Fridays for 1998, with Saturdays and Sundays separately. They are shown by hour of the day. It shows what many would anticipate as the result for the peak hours, but also the extent to which traffic is retained at other periods. During the midday off-peak period, it is of interest to note that Saturday traffic, which has a slow start, overtakes Mondays to Fridays between 11.00 and the beginning of the afternoon peak from 15.00. Sunday traffic mirrors that of Saturday, but at rather lower levels throughout.

Such analyses may, of course, be made for groups of stations as well. However, this gives a network view of what is happening at different times.

Random Disturbances

The only defence which a timetable planner can put up to random disturbances in operations is to allow some judicious spare in his compilation of running and turnround times, to make sure that the operation is not overstretched. This allows recovery from modest delays to be taken in the operator's stride. Small perturbations will always happen, but they can be overcome with a little forethought.

Of other factors in timetable production, account must be taken of the provision of special workings for various purposes. Is it worth while to keep a crewed train on standby on Saturdays for football traffic? If so, where? Even if the train is not crewed, units positioned at strategic points can be valuable in case of failures. This is clearly quite an expensive option, and can work only within the same line or group of lines. The C stock on the sub-surface lines has universal acceptability and is among the most satisfactory for this purpose because of its crowd-carrying capabilities.

With the best will in the world, though, it cannot allow adequately for unforeseen variations such as demonstrations; such matters have to be dealt with by special traffic notices as and when details become clear. A timetable must, however, be sufficiently robust to be adaptable to take account of incidents which occur, including planned engineering work.

Other than for really exceptional reasons, such as the celebrations on New Year's Eve 1999 and King George VI's Coronation in 1938, London Underground does not operate passenger services during the small hours. This reflects both the low demand levels expected normally and, at least as importantly, the need to occupy the running lines and particularly the tunnel sections for infrastructure maintenance. Time availability is strictly limited; from the close down at around 01.00 to start of

Above: To reach Richmond, the Underground runs over Railtrack lines, and these are shared with Silverlink Metro from Gunnersbury. No 313103 stands in Richmond platforms on 8 December 1998 awaiting departure; the timetables have to suit all parties. *John Glover*

traffic the following morning offers a very limited window of opportunity.

Other decisions must be left to the line management on duty at the time.

Economy in Resource Allocation

What makes an effective and efficient timetable? This is perhaps best answered by considering a small section of that of the Northern Line.

By anybody's standards the Northern is a complicated line for a rapid transit system. There are the two branches of Edgware and High Barnet to the north, the latter having a third single-track stub end branch from Finchley Central to Mill Hill East. The branches merge at Camden Town, and allow trains from either to run by the route via Bank, or via Charing Cross. The two routes come together again at Kennington, and proceed as a twin-track route to the Morden terminus.

Additionally, the Charing Cross branch (only) has the facility of a reversing loop at Kennington, which can be used to return trains whence they came. The running time via Bank is roundly 3min longer than that via Charing Cross. These two factors limit the extent to which one route can be used rather than the other.

The problem is how to run a service which satisfies the business requirement in terms of frequency, at even intervals wherever possible, on all sections of the line. There should also be a choice of Bank and Charing Cross destinations from all the suburban origins, without change of train. The timetable planners

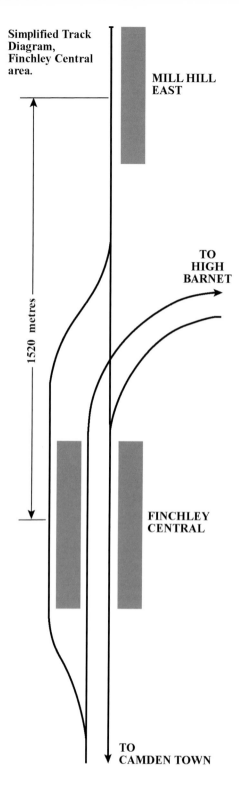

Simplified Track Diagram, Finchley Central area.

MILL HILL EAST

TO HIGH BARNET

1520 metres

FINCHLEY CENTRAL

TO CAMDEN TOWN

have achieved wonders in Working Timetable 47; at the time of writing this has been in force for well over two years. This speaks volumes both for its robustness and its workability. The midday off-peak Monday to Friday service is described below.

The whole is based on a somewhat curious frequency of a train every 4½min, or six trains in a standard 27min period. From the Edgware branch, services run in succession as follows:

- To Morden via Bank
- To Kennington via Charing Cross
- To Morden via Bank
- To Kennington via Charing Cross
- To Morden via Bank
- To Morden via Charing Cross

Thus Edgware branch passengers have a choice, alternately, of a train via Bank and one via Charing Cross. Of the latter, one only goes through to Morden but, as already noted, the extra journey time via Bank is minimal.

From the High Barnet group, trains run thus:

- Mill Hill East to Morden via Bank
- High Barnet to Kennington via Charing Cross
- High Barnet to Morden via Bank
- Mill Hill East to Morden via Charing Cross
- High Barnet to Morden via Bank
- High Barnet to Kennington via Charing Cross.

Here, both the Mill Hill East and High Barnet branches have routes via each of the in-town alternatives, with two of the Charing Cross trains terminating on the Kennington loop.

In a 27min period, there are thus four trains from High Barnet, two from Mill Hill East and six from Edgware. These provide six trains via both the City and Charing Cross, and then eight from Kennington to Morden.

Mondays to Fridays, Timetable No 43

From		Via CX Train No1	Bank 2	CX 3	Bank 4	CX 5	Bank 6
Camden Town	d	13:47.30	13:52.00	13:56.30	14:01.00	14:05.30	14:10.00
Finchley Central	a	14:02.00	14:06.30	14:11.00	14:15.30	14:20.00	14:24.30
	d	14:02.00	14:06.30	14:12.00	14:15.30	14:20.00	14:25.30
Mill Hill East	a			14:14.30			14:28.00
High Barnet	a	14:11.30	14:16.00		14:25.00	14:29.30	

Destination:		Morden	Kennington	Morden	Morden	Morden	Kennington
Via:		Bank	CX	Bank	CX	Bank	CX
Train no:		3	1	2	6	4	5
High Barnet	d		14:22.00	14:26.30		14:35.30	14:40.00
Mill Hill East	d	14:23.00			14:36.30		
Finchley Central	a	14:25.30	14:31.00	14:35.30	14:39.00	14:44.30	14:49.00
	d	14:26.30	14:31.00	14:35.30	14:40.00	14:44.30	14:49.00

Let us now examine in more detail how the High Barnet and Mill Hill East timetable operates. Finchley Central has a second northbound platform, which is used for the Mill Hill East-bound trains. The diagram opposite shows the construction.

From Camden Town northwards, trains adhere precisely to the 4½min frequency. The Mill Hill East trains (only) have an additional minute stand time inserted into their timetables at Finchley Central in each direction; this is necessary to allow a southbound train to clear the single-track branch before a northbound train enters it.

It will also be noted that the Mill Hill East trains arrive from Bank and depart to Charing Cross, and vice versa. As the diagram above shows, the round trip time from Finchley Central is 15½min to Mill Hill East (including stand times) but 29min to High Barnet. Thus the 'change of identity' is needed to maintain a constant Charing Cross/Bank pattern on the southbound run. This also offers a train every 4½ min from Finchley Central. Perhaps the only shortcoming in these arrangements is the alternating 4½ min/9min frequencies on the High Barnet branch which result, but this is perhaps unavoidable.

The whole is of course supplemented by additional peak workings.

What of the rolling stock diagrams, and the distances covered over a day? With a journey time from end to end of the whole line of about 70min, a train can easily make half a dozen or so end-to-end round trips during the working day. Maximum vehicle requirements are as follows:

• Monday to Friday   84 trains
• Saturday   60 trains
• Sunday   55 trains

These are sourced from depots at Morden (by far the largest), Golders Green, Edgware, Highgate and High Barnet. The timetable described uses a maximum of 60 trains.

Non-stopping

Non-stopping of Underground trains through less used stations used to be quite widespread practice. Nowadays it exists only in two cases. One is on the Metropolitan Line north of Baker Street,

Above: The Northern Line at Finchley Central sees a 1995 stock train arriving from Mill Hill East on 21 March 2000. The High Barnet branch (that to Mill Hill East is the main line) diverges to the right just before the rear of the train is reached. The platform on the left is the island. The ramp on the right-hand side beneath the station name is to take the passengers to the bottom of the steps up to the bridge. Platforms here were lowered to suit Underground stock when the line was taken over from the LNER. *John Glover*

where a parallel Jubilee Line exists as far as Wembley Park. Here, the Underground takes on more of the attributes of a 'proper' railway: separate fast and slow services extend as far as Moor Park, and not all stations have platforms on both lines.

The other is between Hammersmith and Acton Town, where the District Line calls at all four intermediate stations in 8min, and the Piccadilly runs nonstop in 6min. Or, almost always. Piccadilly Line trains still make calls at Turnham Green in the early morning and late evening, as a result of which their running time is expanded to 6½min. However, in both of these

instances there are really two parallel railways, to which it is easier to apply varying stopping patterns.

The practice, which came to an end elsewhere on the Underground in the late 1950s, was discontinued because:

- It tends to confuse the public and, sometimes, the staff.
- It is difficult to convey, adequately, exactly what the service pattern is.
- It makes service regulation difficult, in that trains which are nominally non-stopping are in practice often held up by the previous stopping train, and

- Service frequency at the omitted stations falls unacceptably in the evenings and on Sundays.

Line Capacity

It will not have escaped readers' attention that the District Railway was claiming to operate 43tph over 80 years ago, so 36tph as an ultimate achievement with transmission-based signalling (to be described later) seems a little tame. What are the constraints on operating at higher service frequencies?

Train service frequency is determined by seven factors, each of which is a complex issue in itself. These are:

- The train's accelerating and braking capability
- The signalling system
- The degree of stopping accuracy required
- The length of trains
- The time spent stopped at stations
- The terminal station capacity
- The discipline of staff and passengers.

The Train's Accelerating and Braking Capability

The higher the acceleration rate and the longer the duration, the quicker the platform will be cleared and the next train can arrive. In London, an eight-car Central Line train of 1992 stock takes about 19sec between entering a platform and coming to a halt, and about 18sec from starting to clearance of the platform. With a 30sec stopping time, the train is visible from the platform area for a total of 67sec. With a 40tph service, or one train every 90sec, this leaves no more than 23sec before the next train appears. Faster acceleration of the departing train is possible, but might be ruled out on passenger comfort grounds. The focus, therefore, is on the station stop time and aiming to reduce it.

The Signalling System

The train's emergency braking rate, plus the rate at which it may approach a signal, determines the 'overlap' required beyond the signal. The overlap is the minimum safe distance which must be clear beyond a signal before a train may approach it. In London, all trains have an emergency braking rate of at least 1.34m/sec^2 (3mph per second). This typically requires an overlap of 400ft on outer home signals, or 400ft between the signal and the beginning of the platform with a train in it, which it is protecting. Slower trains have to reduce speed less, and 320ft is sufficient overlap if the approaching train is limited to 30mph maximum.

A means of overcoming this limitation by the provision of additional home signals, up to a total of three, was described in Section 3; up to four were at one time used. Together with speed control of the approaching train with yet more home signals, this allowed it to approach very close to the platform provided its speed was reduced sufficiently.

A regulation system is required to ensure trains leave terminals at even intervals. This must suit the desired timetable. For example, a traditional 1950s London Underground 'Programme Machine', which often took the place of a signalman setting routes at terminals, junctions and timing points, moves forwards in 30sec increments. This can be a constraint if the desired headway does not match this. Every 2¼min (27tph) was the Victoria Line peak service for many years. In Paris, everything is geared to 5sec increments, which is essential to operate a reliable, high-frequency service.

The Degree of Stopping Accuracy Required

If the train is significantly shorter than the platform length, stopping accuracy needs to be only approximate. That is rarely the case nowadays. The more accuracy that is required, the less leeway there is and drivers are apt to be a little more cautious. Automatic systems have their benefits, but these will be at their best in dry conditions underground, on platforms without too

Above: The central road at Golders Green has platforms on both sides, which gives some flexibility in terms of opening doors sequentially and thus separating passenger flows. This view is looking north towards Edgware on 21 March 2000. *John Glover*

much curvature. (How much grease is currently being applied to the rail on sharp curves?) Platform monitors enabling drivers to gain visibility down the length of their train are other reasons why accuracy in stopping is essential.

The Length of Trains

The shorter the train, the less time it takes to leave the platform fully. This is a benefit to headway, but not to overall capacity. Shorter trains also clear conflicting junctions more quickly, which is perhaps an indirect benefit. Conversely, if it is planned to increase train lengths, it is important to measure the effect on junction capacity. Nevertheless, the longer that trains are, the greater the carrying capacity for any given service frequency.

The Time Spent Stopped at Stations

This is the most difficult to control and the most significant. The headway is dependent ultimately on the longest time spent at a station stop, even if there is only one stop time which is longer than the rest. Factors which influence it include:

- The time between the train stopping and the passengers being able to alight, which is a function of the door opening time. Passengers could open hand-operated doors before the train stopped. On modern Underground trains, the doors cannot start to be opened unless the train is over a beacon which confirms that all the doors are in the station platform and the train speed is less than 6mph. Also, the driver is unlikely to press the door open buttons until the train has come to a complete stop. There is thus a considerable delay between the train coming to a halt and the doors being fully open.

- The time between the driver wishing to close the doors and being able to start the train is governed by four factors:
1. His waiting for passengers to join the train (if indeed he does). The last few passengers joining an already full train are always that much slower.
2. Actions of passengers holding doors open for others.
3. How quickly the doors actually do shut.
4. The time between the doors being confirmed as properly closed and the train starting.

- The actual stop time, which depends upon the time to operate the doors, the numbers wishing to join, the numbers wishing to alight, and how many stand in the doorways slowing down movement. Problems at stations serving main line railway termini include passengers arriving in large groups as their trains arrive. This can make for excess loads on individual Underground trains, which then spend longer in this and subsequent stations. This can quickly lead to major service disruption.

Where stations are constructed for the purpose with platforms each side of a single track, it is possible to separate those boarding and alighting through use of the doors on each side of the train for different purposes. This used to be practised at Golders Green northbound; one difficulty was the time taken for (in those days) the guard to cross from one side of the car to the other to open the second set, and similarly to close them. It is also possible at Morden, but the problems of termini are different.

The Terminal Station
If the train has to enter at slow speed because of impending buffer stops, this is a particular problem as it is likely to block the station throat to other movements. However, many have over-runs beyond the platform ends, so the problem does not arise. One place where it does matter is Aldgate where the District Line is immediately beyond the stops.

In general, it is difficult to turn more than 30tph in a simple two-platform terminus with a scissors crossover approach such as at Stanmore or Elephant & Castle.

6. Service Provision

Many parts of the Underground are self-contained, with negligible opportunities for running anything other than the services to which users have become accustomed for many years. Thus, Central Line trains run westwards to Ealing Broadway or West Ruislip and eastwards to Epping or Hainault. Even so, life is not quite as simple as it seems; when the Automatic Train Operation (ATO) scheme on the Woodford-Hainault section was abandoned, there was an opportunity to run from central London to Hainault via Woodford or, indeed, to Woodford via Hainault. Both are presently practised.

Nevertheless, there is little scope for more than minor tinkering with service provision on the tube network, short of fairly major expenditure on capital works which offer opportunities to provide new service patterns. The separation of the Bakerloo Line into two, with new

Below: The wide tunnels on the original part of the Metropolitan Railway, seen here at Great Portland Street looking west, had to accommodate the broad 7ft 0¼in gauge of the Great Western. A lasting memento has been what is now the excess width, as seen by the minor incursion of the platform end into the tunnel. A train of C stock arrives on 21 March 2000 on an eastbound (outer rail) Circle Line service. *John Glover*

Above: Interchange between services is helped immensely where cross-platforms can be used. This is Mile End on 15 March 2000, with a westbound Central Line train of 1992 stock. The track on the other side of the island is used by the westbound District and also by the Hammersmith & City Line services. Passengers from the east can thus choose destinations along the Embankment, through the West End via Oxford Circus, or along the Euston Road and the main line termini. No wonder Mile End is a busy station. *John Glover*

construction from Baker Street southwards to create the Jubilee Line in 1979 was one such example. When it comes to the sub-surface network, though, the situation is rather different.

Sub-surface Lines

The Metropolitan, Circle, Hammersmith & City and District lines could, in many ways, be said to form a number of individual train services operating on a unified system. It is, more or less, self-contained as a whole. If, for instance, the track and signalling were to belong to an infrastructure company, and a strategic authority were to invite bids from train operating companies for the provision of services, what service patterns might result?

BAA, the airport authority, expressed an interest in running a Heathrow Express train along the north side of the Circle Line, so that it could serve the City directly instead of just that outpost of central London called Paddington. This brought forth considerable criticism, mostly on the grounds that the Circle was already fully occupied with its present operations. However, the interrelationship of the National Railways system and London Underground has perhaps never been as fully explored as it might be.

Origins

The main lines approached the capital in the early days of railways, with the establishment of Euston more or less on

its present site in 1837. Right from the beginning, what nowadays might be called environmental concerns, or nimbyism, were apparent. There were general fears that the railways would over-run London if left to their own devices. This led to the Royal Commission of 1847, the decision of which effectively barred railways from entering central London. Thus it came about that the northern main line termini are situated along a line from Paddington in the west to Liverpool Street in the east.

The only railway allowed to cross central London was the link from King's Cross via today's Thameslink route through Blackfriars, City Thameslink and Farringdon, and this was to enable the huge wholesale food markets to be served by rail. The nearest Thames railway crossing to the west was the West London line, and to the east was the East London line. That situation remains today.

This left a huge gap in the central area devoid of railways, and the distribution of passengers arriving at Paddington and bound for the City was a task undertaken eventually by the Metropolitan Railway. The first section opened in 1863 and the line was quickly extended. It may be noted here that the Metropolitan was perceived then as just another, albeit specialised, railway. Indeed, it was worked originally by the Great Western and subsequently by the Great Northern, for which physical connections to the rest of the railway network were essential. Later, the Metropolitan became an operating company in its own right. Steam was not replaced by electric traction until the early years of the 20th century.

With the arrival of the Metropolitan District Railway on the scene (a title quickly abbreviated to the District in popular parlance), the network was expanded. Today, it forms the sub-surface lines of the Underground. All were built by cut-and-cover construction to something approaching main line loading gauge and run relatively close to the surface.

With the ability to run through services on the national railway network, services were inaugurated by the District to destinations such as Windsor (very briefly between 1883 and 1885) and to Southend in 1910. This lasted until 1939.

Consolidation and Extension

The sub-surface lines were extended to what became the suburbs, with the Metropolitan Railway being particularly active in this respect. The company's operations extended eventually to Verney Junction in deepest Buckinghamshire, being subsequently trimmed back to Aylesbury and, with the 1960 electrification, to Amersham.

Tube expansion in central London was very active in the Edwardian era. This was later pushed outwards to stimulate suburban growth and, with the help of cheap government finance, to relieve unemployment. The Piccadilly Line to Cockfosters was one example; this work was completed in 1933.

The formation of the London Passenger Transport Board put the Underground railways (which had already become one

Above: This is Liverpool Street on the Metropolitan, 16 March 2000. A stock trains pass on their journeys to Aldgate (right) and from Aldgate (left). The constraints of the location are clearly visible. *John Glover*

group in the Underground Electric Railways of London), the Metropolitan Railway, plus all the tramway and bus interests under one body from 1933. The principal duty of the LPTB (or London Transport as it was known) was:

'to secure the provision of an adequate and properly co-ordinated system of passenger transport for the London Passenger Transport Area, and for that purpose, while avoiding the provision of unnecessary and wasteful competitive services, to take from time to time such steps as they consider necessary for extending and improving the facilities for passenger transport in their area in such a manner as to provide most efficiently and conveniently for the needs thereof.'

The principal activity of the LPTB in the short period left to it before the war was to continue the work of UERL. There

were major rebuildings (eg Holborn and Aldgate East) and, under the 1935/40 New Works Programme, some of the suburban operations of the London & North Eastern Railway and Great Western Railway were assimilated into its own tube system. This saw the inauguration of the Central Line services in the east to Epping and Hainault, and in the west to West Ruislip. The Northern was extended from Archway to High Barnet and to Mill Hill East. These works were not completed until 1949, though part of the ambitious Northern Line plans for new extensions to Elstree were abandoned in the postwar years as being incompatible with Green Belt aspirations and, by then, legislation.

Separation

Henceforth, the Underground grew away from the main line system. Summer weekend excursions such as those from Epping to the south coast via the East

Above: The rear cab of a C stock train on an eastbound Hammersmith & City Line service at Great Portland Street on 21 March 2000. The train is just beginning to move, but there is substantial spare space behind it in terms of platform length, and this is just wasted. *John Glover*

London line fell away in the 1950s, and coal traffic to goods yards on the High Barnet branch was abandoned in 1962.

By the early 1970s, many connections with the national network had been severed. Electrification of the London, Tilbury & Southend prompted a much-needed rationalisation of the railway through Barking and Upminster. The rebuilding of the Paddington approaches was an opportunity to provide physical separation of today's Thames Trains suburban services from the Hammersmith & City Line. Separation avoids the need for technical compatibility and also ensures that 'operational difficulties' on one system (a euphemism for any kind of cock-up) do not affect the other. The East London Line was separated from the national network at both ends, while the Finsbury Park-Moorgate section of the Northern Line was transferred to British Railways in 1975 for its Great Northern electrification scheme.

Today, the only connections remaining are:

- Between Harrow-on-the-Hill and Amersham. Services are operated by Chiltern Railways and the Metropolitan, with joint running over this section.
- Between Gunnersbury and Richmond. Services are provided jointly by Silverlink and the District Line.
- Between East Putney and Wimbledon. South West Trains run empty stock trains between Waterloo and Wimbledon carriage sidings via Point Pleasant Junction, on the Railtrack line via Putney.
- Between Queen's Park and Harrow & Wealdstone. The Bakerloo Line and Silverlink share service provision. Until 1982, the Bakerloo ran to and from Watford Junction.
- At West Ruislip. There is a connection to allow stock transfer to and from the Underground.

Above: The sole surviving Waterloo & City car of 1938 vintage built by English Electric is now at the National Railway Museum at York. On 6 April 2000, it was not on display but was placed alongside a Tunnel Inspection Vehicle. Based on this, one might conclude that the W&C ran in the wrong kind of tunnel! This demonstrates well the incompatibility problems; quite apart from the collision resistance, or lack of it, it would hardly be possible for a disabled train of one sort to be pushed through a tunnel section by the other. *John Glover*

Infrastructure ownership varies between Railtrack and LUL. There are many examples elsewhere on the systems where joint use of stations occurs but there are no physical connections between tracks. Other ownership matters include responsibility for maintenance, power supplies and signalling.

That is the present situation; the results may not be perfect, but services do operate.

Operations

A prime requirement is to make the most of the infrastructure and resources available. Let us start with train service frequency.

Sub Surface lines, central area. Trains per hour, each direction, am peak.

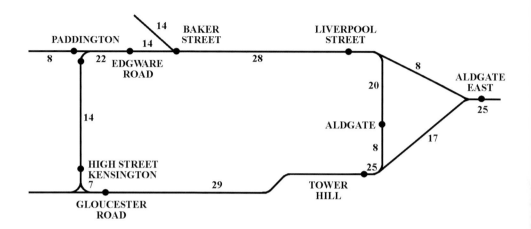

Note that the Circle Line and the Hammersmith & City together operate a 15TPH service. This accounts for the apparent small contradictions in the number of trains per hour at different points.

The diagram above shows the present number of trains per hour in the central area's sub-surface lines at the height of the morning peak; as can be seen, very few stretches have less than 20tph. The two main service groups are operating at just under 30tph. Apart from the very short sections around junctions, the only part which falls much below this is the west side of the Circle Line, where 14tph are offered. It must be stressed that this number of trains operates in *each* direction.

Thirty trains per hour may or may not be the practical maximum on simple systems, but the sub-surface lines are strewn with junctions. The diagram (*above*) shows where these are. The Aldgate station area has already been considered; it is now intended to look more closely at Earl's Court area.

The diagram overleaf shows the track layout of the eastbound line at Earl's Court (the westbound line is not shown). Each of the figures indicates the number of trains per hour during the morning peak on the section concerned. The first conflict, other than from converging lines, is at the east end of the platform, where services proceeding towards High Street Kensington separate from those to the City. But the real problem comes where the Circle Line is reached, in each of two locations. The services arriving from Earl's Court have to intermix with the 7tph Circle in each direction, and those via Gloucester Road also have to avoid the outer rail or clockwise Circle.

In summary, Earl's Court demonstrates a 33tph eastbound service arriving at the station from four different origins and continuing to three different groups of

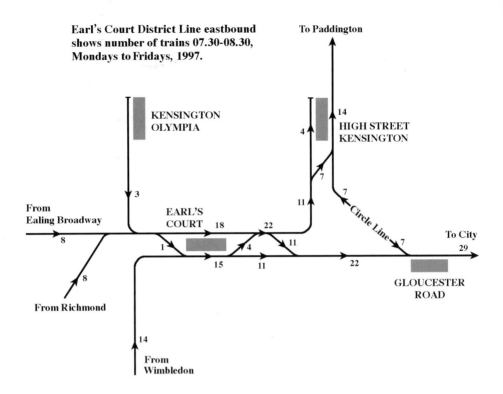

Earl's Court District Line eastbound shows number of trains 07.30-08.30, Mondays to Fridays, 1997.

To Paddington

KENSINGTON OLYMPIA

HIGH STREET KENSINGTON — 14

4

7

3

11

7

Circle Line

From Ealing Broadway

EARL'S COURT   18   22

8

1   4   11

To City

29

15   11   22

GLOUCESTER ROAD

8

From Richmond

14

From Wimbledon

destinations, with the need to fit in with Circle Line operations. The whole operation takes place at grade.

It might be added that the only two grade-separated junctions on the whole of the central area sub-surface system are here. One keeps the High Street Kensington to Earl's Court services below the level of the District main line services. The other is west of Earl's Court, where westbound trains to Richmond etc avoid the eastbound trains from Wimbledon by a steeply-graded diveunder. Effectively, these diveunders separate eastbound and westbound trains completely, save only the junction for Kensington Olympia.

The difficulties associated with the Aldgate area have already been discussed. Given the present operational problems, the scope for running more trains over such a complex network as this seems likely to be very limited, short of a truly major revision to service patterns.

Difference in Emphasis

The British Transport Commission's London Plan Working Party reported in 1949. This group was at pains to distinguish between what it called the urban and outer suburban services, which it then discussed in detail.

The prime task of the high-frequency urban railway services was the mass movement of passengers over short distances, including to and from the inner suburbs. These were defined as those between 10 and 12 miles from the centre of the central area — usually considered to be Charing Cross. Urban services were expected to offer up to 40 trains per hour, to stop frequently, and to have trains with ample standing space and many doors, at the expense of seats.

The outer suburban services were seen as having comparatively high speeds and high seating capacity, but at a lower service frequency, in the order of 25 trains per hour.

A further conclusion was 'that an outer suburban type service cannot at the same time fulfil efficiently the function of an urban-type service in the in-town area'. In other words, you mix them at your peril! The Working Party was also at pains to point out that short-distance passengers crowding out longer-distance passengers was less than desirable.

The Report was written in the year that the Central Line electrification to Epping was completed, which is used in the table below. Wickford, Essex, is served by First Great Eastern from Liverpool Street.

This shows what happens when an urban-type service is projected into the outer suburbs some 27km from central London, and how it compares with a 'true' outer suburban service. It might also be added that the Underground's 1992 stock on the Central Line is noted for its hard and upright seats, which are now completely devoid of armrests. First Great Eastern's Class 321 stock is altogether more comfortable and it offers First Class accommodation for those who wish to use and pay for it.

Service Usage and Customer Profiles
The busiest section of London Underground is, not surprisingly, that within fare Zone 1. The diagram below shows barrier counts of those entering LU stations over the whole working day, in 1990. Each vertical line next to a station

Peak journeys to Liverpool Street	from Epping	from Wickford
Distance, km	27	46
Time, min	40	37 to 42
No of trains, 07.30-08.30	8	10
Intermediate stops	12	between 1 and 4

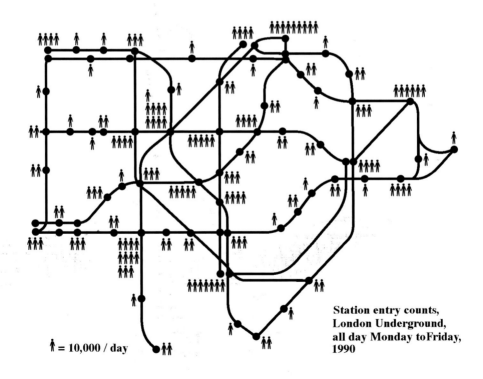

i = 10,000 / day

Station entry counts, London Underground, all day Monday to Friday, 1990

Above: This sign is to be found in the Bakerloo entrance to Elephant & Castle station; there is just a touch of nimbyism about it. More seriously, what should be the Underground's attitude to providing conveniences? The picture was taken on 14 December 1999. *John Glover*

represents 10,000 persons, but it does not indicate in which direction they are about to travel, or on which line where there is a choice.

There are three main points to be noted:

- The West End dominates in terms of the total numbers.
- The other dominant numbers are those joining the Underground at main line stations, particularly those to the south and east of the capital, where the majority of commuters originate.
- The City, although an important source of commuter traffic, has little appeal for leisure travellers, and thus the 'whole day' figures are relatively low.

This is, of course, only part of the picture; the sections of the sub-surface lines in the central area with the highest traffic levels are St James's Park to Sloane Square and, less busy, Baker Street to Euston Square.

In comparison, let us now look at an outer suburban location, in which National Railways also operate. The location is the Great Northern Line north of Finsbury Park, plus the northern outposts of

London Underground's Piccadilly and Northern lines.

The situation here is very different. At all stations north of Finsbury Park, the barrier counts on the Piccadilly Line were recording 10,000 or more passengers at Manor House, Turnpike Lane and Wood Green, dropping to 7,000 at Bounds Green and 5,000 at Arnos Grove and Southgate. This dropped further to 3,000 at Oakwood and 2,000 at Cockfosters. On the Northern Line, the stations at Highgate, East Finchley and Finchley Central managed a minimum of 6,000, with Woodside Park and High Barnet 3,000. Totteridge was down to 1,000 and West Finchley and Mill Hill East 1,000 each.

On what was then part of British Rail, the situation was far less promising. The only stations south of Stevenage (itself with 4,000) which had 2,000 or more passengers entering them during the whole day were Potters Bar, Hatfield and Welwyn Garden City. There were none at all on the Hertford North branch. Most of the rest scored around 1,000, but there were too many at 500 or less. The surveys were made in 1990/1. It is

Above: The avoidance of flat junctions is very helpful to line capacity; this is where the earlier Central Line route from Ealing Broadway, seen here with a 1992 stock train approaching, leaves the later route to West Ruislip. On the right is the former Great Western Birmingham main line, now reduced in this area to single track. The date is 19 December 1998, the location North Acton Junction. *John Glover*

interesting to note the history of these lines: the Great Northern Railway and subsequently the London & North Eastern Railway opposed the projection of the Underground north of Finsbury Park, fearing the effects on its traffic. Later, though, these parts of the Northern Line ceased to be LNER branches from Finsbury Park and instead became part of the Underground in 1940/1. Although traffic north of Finchley Central is weaker, Northern Line traffic levels in general appear to be much more robust than those of the erstwhile parent.

For whatever reasons, a decade ago these British Rail services were not attracting significant numbers of shorter-distance passengers.

Combined Operations?

If there is thought to be more scope for Underground and National Railways trains to run on the same tracks, a number of issues need to be addressed.

Most, though not quite all, National Railways trains approach London in the peak hours formed of anything from eight to 12 vehicles, 20m or, occasionally, 23m long. This makes them far longer than their Underground equivalents. Why run short trains, when a longer one may still take up only one train path? The comparative length of trains has already been discussed; the longer A stock trains, running to Amersham, Uxbridge and Watford, are no more than 6½ 20m-vehicle equivalents. This is a serious shortcoming, as unless the Underground

Above: Platform ends are nowadays well protected, as this photograph of the northbound platform of Finchley Road shows. The signalling allows trains from the Metropolitan (left) to run on the Jubilee (right), as indicated by the junction signal. The date is 20 March 2000. *John Glover*

might lead to some weeding out of existing stations.

However, station platforms, entrances and exits must all be of sufficient dimensions to cope with the volume of passenger traffic anticipated, and stations would almost certainly require to be double ended with entrances and exits at both ends of the platforms. Station platform width poses some considerable problems in cut-and-cover territory, since it is undesirable to undermine the fronts of street buildings when providing more platform space!

The train design must also be conducive to high-speed loading and unloading, which means plenty of doors and available circulating and standing space. The A stock is perhaps still one of the best compromise designs for urban and outer-suburban work; this was a matter to which the CrossRail design team gave much constructive thought.

On more technical matters, high acceleration and deceleration rates, with a relatively modest top speed, are needed for urban work, compared with high maximum speeds and less emphasis on acceleration for trains used primarily in outer suburbia.

Unless only one type of rolling stock is used, there may be variations in the train-to-platform gaps; crashworthiness also becomes an issue, while signalling power supply requirements must be compatible. National Railways stock is also rather heavier.

Finally, there must, of course, be a means of making connections to the main line network. Paddington would be among the easiest to arrange for trains from the Great Western lines, but a destination is also required. The short-lived connection from the eastbound Metropolitan at Liverpool Street to the Great Eastern disappeared completely under the Broadgate development, and Aldgate is too cramped for anything longer than the A stock. Maybe something would be possible at Moorgate, assuming that Thameslink

system can be enlarged to accommodate longer trains, capacity on any present TOC services would be seriously restricted. This result is clearly untenable.

Major civil engineering work would be required for platform lengthening at Underground stations, sometimes to the extent that two stations could perhaps be combined into one. The CrossRail scheme's 'Liverpool Street' station for its 12-car trains stretched as far west as Moorgate in terms of station entrance locations; a similar result elsewhere

Above: Underground services may allow interchange within the premises, but this can be somewhat contrived. At Whitechapel, the westbound District Line platforms seen here on 16 March 2000 have a subway connection to the East London Line, below, and steps up to the footbridge and way out. The East London Line itself passes at right angles, below the girders to be seen at the platform ends. *John Glover*

services are all eventually rerouted via Blackfriars. Extension onwards to the LT&S line, with an ultimate destination of Southend, might be possible. Train path availability, or not, on the Railtrack network, is another matter.

This is a long list of hurdles, but this does not mean to say that they cannot be overcome given time and especially willpower.

The Future

The trends over recent years have shown passenger traffic growth throughout the railway industry, including London Underground; all the indications are that this growth will continue, though it is linked inextricably with the economic performance of Britain in general and London in particular. London's population, too, is expected to rise.

Expansion on the Underground saw the Victoria Line in the 1960s with fewer stops (and hence higher point-to-point speeds), reducing journey times with new routeings. An important feature of the Victoria Line engineering design was that there are no permanent speed restrictions on the running lines. It was also the first, and fairly successful, attempt to produce a 'no hands' railway of some importance, with automatic driving of trains and programme machine control of the signalling.

The Victoria Line did suffer, though, from economies in construction, which made the station platforms rather narrow. Running tunnel diameters are also constrained, which can produce uncomfortable rushes of air in a moving train.

The Jubilee Line extension of the last century (just!) has made a point of

designing for future growth, with allowance for an additional car length in the station design as well as very adequate escalator provision and platform doors. Tunnel diameters are also larger.

Britain does not have the monopoly of wisdom on underground railway developments. What infrastructure development possibilities might there be? Suggestions drawn from overseas undertakings include:

- Separating eastbound and westbound lines on underground sections by placing each at a different level, but both as double track. This allows two tracks with fast and slow trains in each direction. The new construction would be below the existing.
- As before, but at junctions only, with conventional single track at each level. This would allow grade-separated movements.
- Construct a third centre track, bi-directionally signalled, to allow fast and slow trains in the peak direction of travel.
- Move tracks further apart and move platform edges, to allow wider-bodied cars to be used.
- Be prepared to consider new solutions, such as changing from left-hand to right-hand running to solve a particular physical or routeing problem.
- Use buses as rail replacements during the off-peak, to penetrate the local centres better and generate leisure travel.

Some of these are likely to be practicable only when building from new, but there are always other means of fulfilling objectives.

Integration

How might National Railways be integrated with the Underground? As matters stand, the systems are almost completely separated: the rolling stock is not compatible, platforms are likely to be inadequate in both dimensions and access, and a whole host of technical matters need attention. Only long-term planning and heavy investment over a period could lead to more and sufficient uniformity in the future. No assets last for ever, and replacement could move gradually to a single standard.

However, is that a good idea, and do we want it? Both the urban and outer-suburban types of railway as defined in 1949, or amended as one thinks fit, have their niche. Neither can really do the task of the other, in terms of rolling stock characteristics, stopping patterns, service provision levels or overall speeds. We have perhaps been less clever than we could have been in making the distinction between the two, and also in catering for the middle ground. Mixing the best of both worlds is also likely to combine the worst of both.

The so far abortive CrossRail scheme development showed that requirements for even train loadings and the maximum clearance of passengers from platforms in the underground section would be difficult to meet in conjunction with the desired mix of semi-fast outer suburban and stopping inner suburban services.

There is also the question of different levels of usage. The example given

Above: West Hampstead has often been considered as a site for a large-scale interchange; there are stations on the Jubilee Line, the North London (for Silverlink) and Thameslink. Missing, however, is any station on the Metropolitan or Chiltern Railways. A few of the signs on the Jubilee Line station have recently gained these additional directions, photographed on 20 March 2000. *John Glover*

concerned Great Northern services and the Underground, but similar effects can be found in many other parts of the London area. It is suggested that image plays a large part here. Everybody wants the Underground. It is seen as *a good thing*. The Royal Borough of Kingston Upon Thames undertook a study in 1989, which was aimed at linking the Richmond and Wimbledon branches of the District. A new service would be

provided through Kingston, via the present South West Trains route. The running time gains compared with using SWT and changing to the Underground at Vauxhall or elsewhere were derisory, but it was thought that the Underground would provide a service without changes of train, which would also be more frequent.

If a more frequent service is feasible on what more or less amounts to the present network, why should the Underground be thought likely to provide it if South West Trains were unwilling? Well, Underground trains always are frequent, aren't they?

Perhaps two-thirds of the adults in the entire country carry an Underground map with them — in their diaries. That is market penetration of the first order. The Underground is portrayed as simple to use, with a limited number of well-defined lines between which it is easy to interchange to make any desired journey.

The Underground is also perceived as punctual; as there are seldom any timetables displayed other than the 'every three to five minutes' variety, the users don't know or even care whether the train is late or not. They also don't realise that it can be a relatively slow means of getting around over longer distances. On the other hand, you have to use a complicated timetable to find out *when* trains on National Railways run, and *where* they run — if you can be bothered to do so, that is. Anyway, their trains are always late, as the media keep telling you. Besides, what use is a frequency of only twice an hour in an urban environment?

Such caricatures are exaggerated, but to the extent that they exist they are not helpful to the industry. How many readers could draw from memory anything like as good a map of Connex Metro services as they might those of the Underground? Do National Railways present the right image, and to the extent that they do not, how should one go about changing it? Is it even in London Underground's interests to forge too close a link?

There was once an organisation which decided to begin drawing attention to itself by painting all its lamp posts red. The idea was that Network SouthEast would eventually become as well known to the public as London Underground.

Multi-modal Integration

Government policy, as expressed in the 1998 White Paper, comes down firmly on the side of integration between modes. In some ways, this has been pursued in the London situation for years. Sometimes it seems, though, that the buses and the Underground still act largely independently.

The Underground is weak in non-radial services, as the London Transport Market Report of 1998 freely admits. Outside the central area, Underground lines are predominantly radial in character; other routes such as the Piccadilly between Acton Town and Rayners Lane are not among the most prosperous.

Yet, surely there is a market for orbital routes? The answer may well be in the affirmative, but not perhaps to the extent that justifies a metro-type operation. Railways are costly to build, operate and maintain. This is quite acceptable where passenger flows are heavy; the railway is a superb mover of large volumes. The difficulty comes in justifying the provision and maintenance of a specialised right of way for relatively light flows which might be handled adequately by bus.

For many years, London has had a dense bus network, to the extent that every Underground station is now served by a bus route. The last to gain one was Woodside Park, on the High Barnet branch. It follows that buses could be used as links between Underground stations as

Below: A 251 bus pulls away from the bus stop immediately outside Burnt Oak station on 21 March 2000, with Mill Hill, Totteridge and Arnos Grove station on its blind. As far as the author is aware, this facility for reaching other Underground stations is not positively advertised in any way; customers have to use the standard bus map or local version thereof, and work it out for themselves. *John Glover*

Above: Interchange is not always simple. These busy bus stops are situated conveniently close to a Golders Green station entrance. Sadly, London Underground management, in its infinite wisdom, has decided to close this entrance permanently, and a weary trek round the corner is now necessary. Moral: if you are on the 82 bus (left) and want to go towards Victoria, stay on it! The date is 21 March 2000. *John Glover*

part of a journey involving two or even more lines.

Bus Route 251, Edgware to Arnos Grove

This is indeed often the situation, for which the long-established 251 bus route is used as an example. The eastern terminus is outside Arnos Grove Piccadilly Line station, and the bus runs west to Totteridge & Whetstone (Northern Line, High Barnet branch), Mill Hill Broadway (Thameslink) to Burnt Oak (Northern Line, Edgware branch), and Edgware itself. This service runs at 15min intervals over a 17hr traffic day, though the frequency is reduced to 30min during the evenings and on Sundays. Sunday traffic hours are also a little less.

Neither are timings outrageously slow. In fact, they compare quite well with Underground lines which have close station spacing, such as the Hammersmith branch of the H&C. The standard time allowances, by route section, are as follows:

Arnos Grove to Totteridge & Whetstone	9min
Totteridge & Whetstone to Mill Hill Broadway	16min
Mill Hill Broadway to Burnt Oak	7min
Burnt Oak to Edgware	11min

Furthermore, changing buses can extend such journeys to a new set of destinations. Thus interchange at Burnt Oak to a 114 bus will take the passenger to Queensbury (Jubilee Line), Kenton (Bakerloo Line and

Silverlink Metro), Harrow-on-the-Hill (Metropolitan Line and Chiltern Railways), South Harrow (Piccadilly Line) and Ruislip (Metropolitan and Piccadilly lines). The buses either serve the stations themselves or use stops which are very close, although there is some scope for improvement. Similarly, a journey on a 34 bus eastwards from Arnos Grove will deposit a passenger at Walthamstow Central, Victoria Line.

Such services are not marketed as being complementary to the Underground network; perhaps they should be. Does the average Underground passenger really regard the bus as a mode of transport worth considering? It is not slow. Even a longish journey such as Arnos Grove to Edgware by the 251 bus takes just 43min from end to end. This compares with a running time of 45min by Underground, changing at King's Cross and incurring

additional interchange and waiting time on top of that. It will also be much cheaper for the passenger, though this may be of less significance where a Travelcard is held.

This discussion is not aimed at diminishing the role of the Underground, but the fact needs to be faced that there are some tasks at which it can never excel. Just as the main line railways have reinvented bus connections to create new journey opportunities, it should not be assumed that the London system is as well organised and promoted as it might be. In National Railways, this situation was perhaps accelerated by the influx of bus-based businesses such as First Group and National Express as Train Operating Company franchisees. Would the creation of a link between Underground operators and bus operators be similarly productive?

7. A Simple Railway

This chapter considers one line only, surely the simplest of all. This is the Waterloo & City, running between Waterloo and Bank.

The Waterloo & City Line is a child of the London & South Western Railway, being the access to the City for that company's passengers. It was opened in 1898. The line was transferred to London Underground on 1 April 1994, rather than becoming part of Railtrack.

This is a simple two-tracked railway, with two stations only at Waterloo and Bank. The distance between them is 1 mile 46ch (or 2.37km) and the journey time 4min eastbound and 3¼ min westbound. The track layout is shown in the diagram below.

As will be seen, trains from the Waterloo reversing siding proceed to Platform 25, where they load. They then run to Bank, where there is a scissors crossing leading to an island platform, albeit that each track and platform is in a separate bored tunnel, with connecting passages between them. The two platforms are used alternately, to even out the wear on the pointwork. It also helps spread passengers around the premises.

After a minimal stand at Bank to allow passengers to detrain or join, trains return on the other track. After discharging their passengers at Waterloo, they proceed to the single reversing siding and the whole sequence begins again.

The rolling stock capacity and the headway between trains determine the capacity of the Waterloo & City trains. The four-car trains of 1992 stock clones seat 136 passengers at 34 per car, and counts by the author suggest that a standing load of about 100 per car on top of that is the practical maximum. A peak load of around 500 per train is a good performance. It follows that, at a 3¼ to 3½ min frequency, or 18 trains per hour, the line can convey around 9,000 people in each direction per hour. This is of course partially dependent on when people present themselves for travel; in the 'towards Bank' direction in the morning, this is related to the arrival of South West Trains services at Waterloo. In the evening, it is more related to passengers targeting a particular train to catch home. It should perhaps be mentioned here that the flows in the opposite direction from Bank in the morning and from Waterloo in the evening are nothing like as dense.

The whole is a tight operation, provided by five trains, of which four are in use during the peaks and three in the interpeak period. This reduces to two on Saturdays and later on Monday to Friday evenings. The complete round trip for a train takes about 12min.

What are the constraints on capacity? Imagine a journey in the morning peak. At Waterloo, the train arrives from the

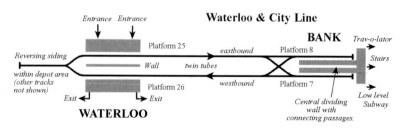

Waterloo & City Line

Entrance Entrance

Platform 25

Reversing siding

within depot area (other tracks not shown)

Wall   *twin tubes*

easthound

BANK   *Trav-o-lator*

Platform 8

Stairs

Platform 26

westbound

Platform 7

Exit   *Exit*

WATERLOO

Central dividing wall with connecting passages.

Low level Subway

Above: The turnback siding at Waterloo on 8 August 1998 sees a 1992 stock train beginning to move forward to enter the eastbound platform. A second train is in the maintenance area. *John Glover*

reversing siding. It then takes time to load. Long queues have formed in the subways which lead to the platforms. The longer the train is stationary, the more line capacity it occupies. The throughput is dependent upon the time taken for each stage of the round trip journey. If a train has the capacity for 'catching up' the train in front and is delayed as a result, that is a pinch point. However, this concerns much more than technical performance, as will be demonstrated. Thus, not only is the time spent in the platform important, but also the rate of boarding. Passengers are not always willing to enter an even moderately crowded train. As Sir John Elliot, the then LT Chairman, once famously remarked: 'They're not crammed in, they cram themselves in.' It is noticeable that passengers are sometimes

unwilling to board if they themselves will be at the platform edge for the next train, and thus be certain of securing a seat rather than stand in some discomfort. They also know that the next train will be along in about 3min.

On arrival at Bank, after suffering a slow approach to ensure that the train is properly under control before entering a dead-end platform, the doors open and the train discharges. This has to be achieved with passengers shouldering their way past those waiting to join. The only exits are beyond the eastern end of the platforms; they consist of the original stairway tunnel to the Underground ticket hall and subway area, the parallel 1960 travolator, and a low-level walkway to the Northern and Central lines, the Docklands Light Railway, and the Circle

and District lines at Monument. Even so, the Waterloo & City train can be on its way again and back to Waterloo in as little as 45sec.

There is also a problem in the time it takes to clear the platforms from incoming commuters at Bank. The platforms are not over-wide, so the situation can arise that a second train arrives before passengers from the first have completely cleared. That is the real limit to line capacity; it will apply however sophisticated the signalling and however slick the operation.

Congestion is perhaps at its most serious in the evening peak. Especially if the service is operating irregularly (for whatever reason), steps have to be taken to restrict those entering the platforms at Bank on safety grounds. This may be achieved by shutting off the stairway from the ticket hall and subway area, and stopping the down direction travolator. That in the up direction remains in use for those arriving from Waterloo. Adequate staffing for such tasks is absolutely essential.

Station times at Bank increase because of the sheer weight of numbers on the platforms, which slows those alighting and who then have to make their way to the exit through the mass of people. The driver also has to make his way from one end of the train to the other, though 'stepping back' can ease this. At the cost of an additional driver, the arriving driver drops a train and takes the subsequent one out, thus giving him extra time to make his way to the far end of the platform. Meanwhile, the train in question is taken away by the driver of the previous one, and so on.

In theory this gives additional train capacity as measured in places per hour, but there are problems:

- There is a need to allow time for people to alight from the train, but also to clear the station, particularly at Waterloo in the evening. Trains may be held in the tunnel short of Waterloo, awaiting the platform to be cleared and the preceding train to move to the reversing siding.
- The crossover at Bank will allow some movements in parallel, but others will conflict and cannot be undertaken simultaneously.

What therefore can be done to increase the capacity? From the above, it will be clear that it is not just the capacity of the train but also that of the stations. Also, LUL cannot control the rate at which people present themselves for travel. It will already be apparent that effective solutions to a growing market are likely to be exceedingly expensive and disruptive during their execution.

The Trains
- Increasing train capacity might be arranged by lengthening platforms to take eight-cars rather than four-cars, though there may be physical restrictions in terms of building foundations, for instance.
- Double-deck trains of the same present overall length would cause a prolonged suspension of operations during work to enlarge the tunnels, while boarding and alighting times would increase.
- Seats could be removed from trains to increase standing space, apart from a

Above: The 1992 stock on the Waterloo & City is still in Network SouthEast livery, if trains with a blue front can so be called. It certainly isn't in Underground corporate colour scheme, even though the basic colours are much the same. This is 8 August 1998. *John Glover*

token few over the wheels for the disabled, subject to the ability to rehouse other under-seat equipment.
- Each train can be double-crewed, with a driver permanently stationed at each end. This eliminates the time for staff to change ends in the platform at Bank and along the reversing siding at Waterloo.

The Signalling
- Signalling enhancements such as moving block can increase line capacity. With other enhancements, this could allow the operation of driverless trains as on the DLR.

The Station Platforms
- Separate platforms could be built at Bank for arriving and alighting passengers to keep the flows separate, though this is likely to take longer if the doors on each side of the train are opened in sequence rather than simultaneously. New passenger access

tunnels would also be needed.
- Station platforms could be widened to increase the numbers of passengers which they could hold safely at any one time.

Platform Access
- Further pedestrian tunnel(s) could be built, but LUL would not be thanked for pushing a new passageway access through the vaults of the Bank of England, or any other of the major banks in the vicinity. They would also have to discharge passengers into a busy sub-surface subway system.
- Lifts to the surface avoiding interchange facilities might be constructed if a suitable site could be found with adequate access.

Alternatives
- The rail alternative for many years has been use of the Central and Northern lines, changing between them at

Tottenham Court Road, but this is very
time-consuming and each of these lines
is busy anyway. Although still
recommended as the alternative, travel
by Northern Line from Bank to London
Bridge and thence by Jubilee Line to
Waterloo is much quicker at about
15min including access and waiting
times. Other routes include using
Connex from Cannon Street via London
Bridge and thence to Waterloo East.

The above are to some extent
interdependent. Reference has been made
earlier to the pinchpoint problems which
need to be solved. But eliminating or at
least easing one of them will then throw
up problems elsewhere. The railway has to
be treated as a system, which is only as
strong as its weakest link. Credit also
needs to be given to the railway's
management and staff, in whose hands the
efficiency and safety of the operation lie.

The example of the Waterloo & City has
been quoted at length, as it represents a
microcosm of what happens to some
extent at many locations on LUL and
indeed throughout the world on similar
systems. However, the real capacity
problems are confined to the periods at
the height of the peak. This lasts for a total
of perhaps two hours in each of the
morning and evening periods, or four
hours a day — and five days a week. The
Waterloo & City operates for 15½hr a day
Mondays to Fridays and 10½hr on
Saturdays. LUL introduced a Saturday
afternoon service, which was the first time
this had been provided for many years.
There is no Sunday service.

There is little doubt that any work to
resolve the situation will:

- Be costly.
- Take time to implement, given the need
  for consultation with interested parties,

the likely need to obtain legal powers,
the design stage, the arrangements for
funding, the construction time and,
ultimately, commissioning.
- Cause major service disruption while in
  progress.
- Need to be undertaken to cater for a
  problem which lasts for around 20hr out
  of the 168hr in a week, or a mere 12%
  of that time.

The justification for such work is hardly a
business one. The problem is social and
has to be funded accordingly. Waterloo to
Bank and vice versa is not a journey made
much outside business hours, or for
pleasure purposes. The main exception
perhaps concerns the Lord Mayor's Show,
but one cannot build an economic case on
an event on one Saturday each November.
It is not as if total line capacity is
insufficient; the root problem is that
demand is so highly concentrated into two
short periods of the working day. The
fleets of trains perhaps exemplify that the
case for investment has always been

Above: Waterloo & City car No 57 was on display at Waterloo main line on 1 October 1988. This view shows well the limited door openings (one single and one double) in the side of this driving motor coach, and also the loss of saloon space caused by the inability to accommodate all the traction gear below the frames. The net result was that entry and exit from the cars was very slow compared with the 1992 tube stock used today. *Peter Ashton*

difficult to make. The original trains built for the 1898 opening were not replaced until 1940, and these units had to last until 1993. While the longevity speaks well for their quality of construction and maintenance, most railways built in the 19th century have had their stock replaced more than twice by the 21st century.

Another major consideration is the forecast of future demand levels, which are presently growing. This is a function of the state of the national economy in general and that of the City in particular. How will this change over the next decade, and the decade beyond that? Will the numbers travelling rise, remain much the same, or fall? It is important that such questions are explored as far as possible, since there are no prizes for getting the answers wrong in one's investment plans.

Whether or not readers will agree with the title of this chapter is for them to decide, but even the simplest have their problems!

Right: Of all the unlikely places to find a wagon turntable, the Waterloo & City Line depot at Waterloo is perhaps it. These were used mostly in constricted industrial premises to move wagons to and from loading bays, by capstan, horsepower or manpower. Here, in the workshops, it is understood that is was used to move car bogies when separated from the saloons. This picture was taken on 8 August 1998. *John Glover*

Above: A train of 1992 stock arrives at Bank on 13 April 1999, just as the evening peak is beginning to get under way. *John Glover*

Left: The passengers on the Waterloo & City make for the subway exit at Waterloo, which takes them to the main line station platforms. The train will now proceed to the turnback siding. The date is 13 April 1999. *John Glover*

The Stations

The station is an integral part of the railway; besides allowing people to board and alight from trains, it also offers the opportunity to purchase the tickets. It is the revenue from this transaction which sustains the entire operation.

Station spacing is rather more varied than many appreciate; there are 16 pairs of stations 500m or less apart, of which all but two pairs (Canada Water and Rotherhithe, and South Ealing and Northfields) are in central London. It

could be argued that this is not really necessary. They are listed in Appendix I.

At the other end of the scale, there are 31 stations 2,250m apart or more. (This does not include pairs such as Baker Street to Finchley Road on the Metropolitan, as the two stations of St John's Wood and Swiss Cottage on the Jubilee are deemed to be in between.) This more varied group includes some stations on the outer reaches of the Metropolitan and also the former LNER branches. The only entry

Below: A 1995 stock train arrives at West Finchley with a southbound working to Kennington via Charing Cross on 21 March 2000. The footbridge is in the background and is normally the only way of reaching the southbound platform from the station entrance and ticket office, left. The Wentworth Avenue entrance is behind the photographer, at the very end of the platform. *John Glover*

Above: Station gardens can hardly be said to be an intrinsic part of railway operations, but they give pleasure to many. Those at Chesham, seen here on 30 August 1998, are among the finest on the system. *John Glover*

wholly in fare Zone 1 is the (complete) Waterloo & City Line. This group forms Appendix II.

There are various parts of the station fabric and services to be considered, and each is dealt with in turn.

Platforms

An important consideration in determining the capabilities of the system is its ability to handle passengers. In other words, there is no point in building longer trains if the resulting passenger numbers cannot be handled at the stations.

The station platform is a key component. In Underground tube tunnels, the platform width (between the platform edge and the back platform wall) is determined by the diameter of the station tunnels. While it is, of course, *possible* to enlarge these by inserting additional segments into the lining, this type of work would be extremely disruptive to operations and correspondingly costly. There is also a geometry problem, in that existing lining segments which together form a circle cannot be adapted to encompass a larger diameter without irregularities resulting.

The platform width requirement of HMRI (Her Majesty's Railway Inspectorate) when approving new stations has increased over the years. Single-faced platforms should not be less than 2,500mm wide, although this may decrease towards the platform ends. There should also be at least 3,000mm headroom at all points. These are part of a long list of guidance for stations on underground systems, in which special attention is given

to access, the safety problems of crowding, emergency exits, lighting and ventilation.

In recent years, there has been a change in emphasis in the guidance given; it is not so much prescriptive as to what has to be done, but concentrates instead on the principles. Thus, under stations, 'platforms should allow for the safe waiting of people, their boarding and alighting from trains'. Ideas of what constitutes good practice follow, but that is not to suggest that other solutions would be ruled out, where the station operator can make out a good case and the basic principles are fulfilled.

It should perhaps be mentioned that the principles and guidance are not retrospective; they apply only to new works and to modifications of existing ones.

The building of the Victoria Line, which finally got the go-ahead in 1962, was to a specification which had been pared down wherever possible. One result was that platform widths suffered; reducing station tunnel diameters mean that much less spoil had to be removed. Some measurements made at a really busy station such as Oxford Circus compared the Bakerloo and the Victoria lines:

Victoria Line, northbound
2,910mm (9ft 6in), throughout
Bakerloo Line, northbound
3,220mm (10ft 7in), reducing to
2,800mm (9ft 2in) at platform ends

Spot checks on the Bakerloo suggested that other station platforms were close to these dimensions, though they might narrow more at the ends. For instance, Lambeth North, northbound, reduces in four steps from 3,320mm to 2,810mm, 1,970mm and 1,590mm. This, however, affects only the very back of the train, which is also that part of the platform furthest from the platform entrance/exit.

There is of course no 'magic' about any of these dimensions, in the sense that one is right and the others wrong. However, maintaining passenger flows is dependent upon there being space for people to manoeuvre. A platform must allow for joining passengers to congregate before their train arrives, and for alighting passengers to leave it. These both need to take place without either group unduly obstructing each other, but more importantly without delaying the train through excessive station dwell time.

It is the case, though, that crowds on platforms rarely spread themselves evenly along the platform length. This may be due in part to the position of the platform entrances and exits, and also the interchange subways, particularly if they are located towards or beyond the platform ends. The more regular travellers may attempt to position themselves with regard to the station exit where they alight or, less commonly, where they think or perhaps know that there is a better chance of finding a seat. This last is more relevant for the long and wearisome homeward journey to the suburbs; those who are going to be on the train for only two or three stations anyway often have little inclination to sit down. On the other hand, visitors to the capital and anybody else who is unsure of where the exit is at their destination station, are less likely to walk along the platform 'on spec'.

Above: An extra-wide platform at Euston, Northern City southbound, is the result of it previously being a single island with a track both sides. There is now plenty of room here for passengers to circulate. The train is of well-worn 1959 stock and the date is 1 September 1998. *John Glover*

Not directly relevant to the Underground, but a feature of the National Railways system, is the 12-car commuter train arriving at (say) Victoria in the morning peak. The only exit from the platform is beyond the front of the train and on to the concourse. The first vehicle is heavily over-crowded, the middle of the train is comfortable, and the last vehicle has seats to spare. Overall, the train may well meet crowding standards of the PIXC (Passengers in Excess of Capacity) variety. This does not stop those in the front of the train feeling aggrieved and complaining accordingly. That the remedy may be in their own hands is of little relevance; to them the railway is failing in what they perceive as its duty to convey them in reasonable comfort. On the Underground matters are usually less extreme, in the

sense that there are few occasions when *all* the passengers alight from really busy trains. Where this does happen, such as on the Waterloo & City Line at Bank in the morning peak and at Waterloo in the evening peak where in both cases the problem is obvious, passengers do take some trouble when boarding to ensure that they spread themselves out along the platform. Even so, there is often a little more room in the train at the points furthest from the exits.

It may always become necessary to discharge a train load of passengers on to an already crowded platform due to some kind of train failure. In such cases, standing densities can be that much higher. However, particularly if this is likely to signify an extended break in operations, it may be necessary to

Above: Station shelters do not have to be grandiose; nobody could accuse this erection on the eastbound platform at North Ealing of being anything more than basic. It keeps the rain off and provides shelter from the wind, so who is complaining? *John Glover*

disperse passengers and advise them to find alternative travel means.

The practicalities of this depend upon the station layout and also the platform widths. Thus, on the Jubilee Line, if southbound services have to be suspended beyond Green Park in the morning peak, the trains can be diverted to the former but now defunct Charing Cross terminus to reverse. However, passengers may have to be 'tipped out' (that lovely user-friendly expression so beloved of LUL staff) at Baker Street. This reflects the limited accommodation at both Bond Street and Green Park, but also the greater range of opportunities available for alternative travel from Baker Street compared with the other two stations. This might be interpreted as a reason to keep Charing Cross Jubilee Line available for passenger

use, but that also means keeping the escalators and the rest of the fabric in good order for what should be no more than a very occasional occurrence. The escalators might find permanent use elsewhere on the system. In such matters there are no easy answers; custom and practice should always be questioned, but it never hurts to reassess the alternatives from time to time.

There are then the secondary considerations, such as what happens when trains at any given platform serve more than one destination (or if some terminate short at [say] Wembley Park rather than continue to Stanmore). The effect of this is that not all passengers join the first available train, but wait for a subsequent one. Thus the platform indicators at St James's Park may show,

Above: Platform doors here, at Canada Water westbound, are still in their early stages of acceptance by the public. The feeling of a station platform is not totally lost, but one might not be surprised to see a few kiosks, given the large amount of available space. This was on 20 March 2000. *John Glover*

successively, Wimbledon, Richmond, Circle and Ealing Broadway. (As it happens, the present dot-matrix indicators allow no more than the next three trains to be shown at any one time, but it is a common sequence of events and many passengers will know this.) However, situations of this sort mean that additional space is required on platforms for waiting passengers; anybody wanting to travel to Chiswick Park or beyond has to wait for the Ealing Broadway train. Or, of course, they could take the Richmond train and scuttle across the island platform at Barons Court to the Piccadilly, for Acton Town or Ealing Common . . . But this perhaps merely demonstrates that there is often more than one way of solving one's travelling problems, and all sorts of unanticipated movements can result.

All the above demonstrates the importance of train indicators, nearly all of which nowadays tell the passenger where (up to) the next three trains are going, and how long they are likely to have to wait. These can be backed up by verbal announcements. Passengers can plan, or sometimes replan, their journeys only on the basis of the information available to them.

Platform Doors

For the first time in London, platform doors have been installed on the Jubilee Line stations Westminster to North Greenwich inclusive. This is a total of eight stations and 17 installations, given that North Greenwich has three platforms. All are underground.

Platform or screen doors provide a barrier between the platform and the track, increasing safety and comfort for passengers by protecting them from the track and moving trains. At least as importantly, screen doors reduce the air turbulence as trains enter and leave the station. The problems of air movement are much reduced. Air quality improves, wind speed is reduced and with it airborne dust.

The provision of doors means that passengers can stand close to what would otherwise be the platform edge in comfort and safety; they also know where the doors of the train will be positioned. Whether this will mean that those boarding trains will be more willing to allow those alighting to do so first remains to be seen; some marking of platforms may be desirable.

The result should be cleaner platform areas, which are quieter and have a temperature-controlled environment.

In operation, the doors rely on the train being positioned correctly before they can be released. With a dry rail and what amounts to controlled conditions, this is likely to be a minimal problem, but would cause difficulties above ground. Precise positioning of trains if rails may be wet or dry, with or without a strong wind blowing, becomes that much more difficult. To ensure merely that the train is fully on the platform, itself with a little spare length to cater for minor inaccuracies, is not enough. Either the train is lined up sufficiently accurately for platform doors and train doors to near enough match up, or it isn't!

One feature aiding installation on the Jubilee Line is that all platforms are either straight or very nearly so. This is certainly far from the case on many other parts of the system, although it was a feature of the Victoria Line. It will be interesting to assess whether there will be pressures for the general fitting of platform doors across the Underground in the future.

Passageways

There is little to say about connecting passages and circulating areas, other than that they need to be treated as part of the overall system. The word bottleneck may be used in many contexts, but in this one it is most appropriate. The movement of people through passages may be likened to the movement of liquids; any narrow point constrains the entire flow. So it is in the Underground environment, and the build-up of passengers on platforms has already been discussed. If the train service is interrupted or delayed for any reason, people will still arrive on the platforms and eventually this becomes a safety hazard.

Flows have to be halted, and this may mean stopping one or both of the escalators. People may be allowed to walk down, but even then the situation can arise when entry to the station is restricted or barred altogether. This type of action can be seen at Holborn in the evenings, where the numbers trying to enter from the street are more than those being allowed to descend to platform level. The pavement outside thus becomes very congested, resulting in a real problem for pedestrians with no interest in the station itself. A variation on this can be seen at Chancery Lane, the next station east on the Central Line. Here, the station is restricted to use for exit only during the morning peak due to inadequate capacity because of escalator replacement.

Other responses to such problems are the non-stopping of trains. This has been done on the Piccadilly Line at Holborn on occasion. Such action also has the effect of stopping the movement of interchange passengers between the lines. To aid enforcement of the matters described in this section Bostwick lattice gates or their equivalent are often installed to shut off part of the premises. This requires staff intervention. Any busy station needs an authority responsible for its operations, such as a duty manager. Ideally, that person will be located in a purpose-built

Above: A station entrance can be inviting, adequate or scruffy. The reader is left to decide which category Highgate, seen here on 24 August 1999, comes into. Use it if you have to! *John Glover*

ticket hall area. CCTV cameras are an effective means of seeing how the situation is developing.

There are well-rehearsed methods of closing and evacuating stations in response to bomb alerts or similar occurrences.

Ideally, the inward and outward flows of passengers, or those between lines, should be kept separate as far as possible. It is always easier to use a passageway when everybody is going in the same direction than where one is meeting those coming towards one. Keep left signs, or keep right as the case may be, seem to have little effect. Even 'no exit' is sometimes defied, if people think it might be a quicker way to where they wish to go — and they may be right. Such groups come unstuck when they meet an escalator which allows movement in the 'right' direction only, but this does not happen often.

Keeping major flows apart is always desirable in the interests of making the best use possible of the station infrastructure, though this is often easier to state as an objective than to put into practice. Even allowing for the activities of the awkward squad, the space constraints are often such that there is no really satisfactory answer.

It all comes down to human behaviour, which is not easily predictable. It is therefore difficult to model. Such restrictions must be realised and assumptions made as to the most likely behaviour.

Within a station complex, observations include:

- People will accept different levels of crowding depending upon the situation. For example, people will tolerate a higher degree of congestion on an escalator for what they know is only a short time. They will be less likely to accept such congestion on platforms.
- Commuters tend to know their way around and will walk by the shortest route. Occasional travellers will take more time looking for signs.

control room with CCTV to monitor the whole station. It will also receive information on approaching times and on the health or otherwise of station equipment. There will also be good communications with the line controller.

Where action such as restrictive measures have to be taken, they need to be controlled with care, to ensure not only that platforms remain safe for the numbers present but also that there is no risk of passengers being crushed should the situation get really difficult. This is likely to mean the deployment of staff to strategic points around the premises, with communication to the station control room. This is most usually situated in the

- Passengers queuing for tickets will order themselves, but queues for escalators or lifts will be less orderly.
- On platforms, greater densities of passengers will be found nearer entrances, as many are reluctant to move along.
- Passenger flow rate is affected by the space available. The greater the space available, up to a maximum, the faster people move.
- Flights of steps slow down flows, which means that the passageway should be wider at this point. If they are not well marked, they are also a potential hazard.
- The broadcasting of military marches over the PA system speeds people along; slow waltzes are to be avoided.

These are not immutable facts. They do suggest, however, that a critical observation of movement problems within stations, with views like these borne in mind, are a useful prelude to planning alterations in passenger flows. It is emphasised that it is always desirable to meet the individual circumstances, rather than to apply a blanket solution.

The extent of stations which are completely underground can be quite difficult to grasp. The diagram below shows the complexities of King's Cross St Pancras as it is presently.

Work associated with the proposed closure of King's Cross Thameslink and its replacement with a new station on the west side of St Pancras, plus the Channel Tunnel Rail Link terminal, is not shown. The Underground station has the operational inconvenience in that it is not possible to move between the tube and sub-surface stations without passing through two ticket barriers and the public area in the subway beneath Euston Road, and this is also being addressed.

Signing

'You can't expect passengers to find their way if you do not give them some help in directions.' Adequate and readable signs, situated where the message can be easily digested, (hopefully) without stopping to

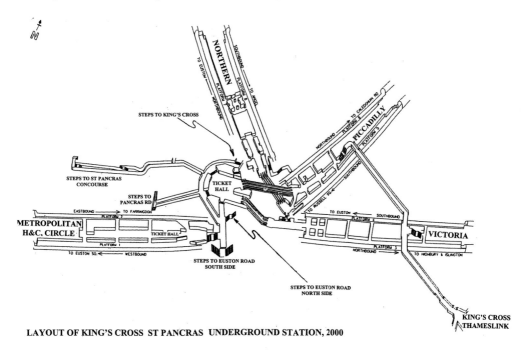

LAYOUT OF KING'S CROSS ST PANCRAS UNDERGROUND STATION, 2000

Above: The Underground has never been short of notices of one sort or another; this pair may be seen at Acton Town, where they were photographed on 6 February 2000. *John Glover*

read it, are a basic requirement. They may take many forms, but the essential feature is that they should not leave the passenger in any doubt as to where to go. Ideally, they should be placed in positions so that they are not obstructed by other travellers, so above people's head level tends to be helpful. A clear typeface is also highly desirable, and in this LT's 'New Johnston' succeeds admirably. The presentation should also be consistent; here the use of not only 'Circle Line' but also the line colour of yellow can help. Signs are there for the benefit of all passengers, and those whose native tongue is not English are likely to find following a colour helpful.

This brings in the question of language and the adaptations to be made. The reality is that space for signage is limited, and introducing say French, German, Spanish and Japanese means first of all that the type size goes down dramatically. Besides, whatever languages are chosen, there will always be many others, which are not. Pictograms may form part of the

answer, but it would appear that the meaning and understanding of these is nothing like as universal as one might be led to believe.

An interesting idea comes from Singapore, where metro stations are identified by (Arabic) numbers as well as names; this is certainly an alternative where different scripts are in common use. In London, might Station 36 be more instantly recognisable to many than Tottenham Court Road, even if the name is repeated all along the platform frieze? The suffix 'east' or 'west' can be added to the number to show the direction, with a colour for the line. There are many ideas from other systems upon which one can draw, and they needn't be prohibitively costly, either.

Station names should be clearly visible from the train, for all passengers. This may be difficult for those sitting in the rear of a train, who may not see a station nameboard for several successive stations. This is being overcome, in part, by digitised speech announcements on board.

Canada Water

From 30 January 2000

A

Westbound train times

Departures to central London from platform 1

Mondays to Fridays	Saturdays	Sundays
0524 *first train*	0524 *first train*	0718 *first train*
0534 41	0534 44 54	0725
	0600	
then every	*then every*	*then every*
3 to 5	**3 to 5**	**3 to 5**
minutes until	*minutes until*	*minutes until*
0017	0017	2318 24 34
0028 *last train*	0028 *last train*	2345 *last train*

Above: Service information may be quite rudimentary, as in this example for the Jubilee Line at Canada Water on 20 March 2000. Does it actually matter that minutes past the hour are not available? For most passengers, this probably only becomes important at the end of the day, when frequencies also diminish and they are interested in connecting with, perhaps, a long-distance main line service. *John Glover*

Above: Stations need to be maintained, and good design suggests that horizontal surfaces which can be used to deposit litter should be avoided. This is not a posed shot; the author much prefers coffee to tea! This is on the new Jubilee Line platforms, 20 March 2000. *John Glover*

AUTOMATIC LIFTS
STAND CLEAR OF GATES
DIRECTLY WARNING SOUNDS

THESE LIFTS ARE ARRANGED TO GIVE A ONE MINUTE
SERVICE. PASSENGERS ARE REQUESTED NOT TO PREVENT
THE DOORS FROM CLOSING, AS THIS HOLDS THE LIFTS
AND CAUSES DELAY OF ONE MINUTE TO PASSENGERS
ALREADY IN THE LIFT

Above: Some of the less satisfactory aspects of lifts are made clear by this notice, now in the care of the London Transport Museum. A one-minute service may sound frequent, but you can travel a long way on an escalator in that time. As for people obstructing the doors...
John Glover

In the author's opinion, there is always room for improvement, but having said that, London Underground is streets ahead of many other metro or light rail systems. Good comprehensive signage, it might be added, is not cheap, but it is a very important aid to users.

There are other fixed sources of information, such as the dot matrix indicators on platforms. These seem to have settled down well, although they are better suited to the underground and artificial light environment. A bright spring morning in the very open-air station of Totteridge left the author completely unable to make any sense at all of the indicator, other than to establish that it was in fact working. The adaptation of equipment from one environment to another is not always as simple as it might seem. Placing the indicator under the platform canopy might be a partial solution.

The other method of addressing the captive audience is through public address systems, which need to be audible without too much distortion wherever they are intended to be heard. Again, those living in houses near an above-ground station are less than enthusiastic about platform or station announcements; their discomfiture may also be affected by the prevailing wind direction. In such situations, public address must be used sparingly, and probably not at all between (say) 21.00 and 07.00, other than for any announcements which are absolutely necessary.

Lifts and Escalators

Deep-level tube stations have to be provided with some form of access other than by stairs, and this was recognised from the earliest years. There is a limit as to how many flights of stairs it is reasonable to expect even a moderately fit passenger to mount; having to do so does not exactly enhance the saleability of one's travel product. Today, of course, there is more concern for disabled passengers. In some cases, even the short flights of steps which are often found, as from the street to a ticket hall below ground level, or from a lower-level landing to platforms, are considerable obstacles. Furthermore, the continuously moving escalator does not suit everybody; this includes those with more than minimal baggage, a guide dog or, especially, a pushchair with toddler and all the associated paraphernalia which is likely to be needed.

That said, the very fact that the escalator does keep moving means that waiting times for access are minimal when compared with the lift. Escalators move at around 45m (140ft) per second; any faster, and some people will hesitate when stepping on. Although service is continuous, groups of people awaiting access can and do build up, especially when large numbers have alighted from a train, for instance. Lifts always appear sluggish in comparison; waiting times can be unpredictable and it is not easy to maintain a regularly spaced service. Obstructing the doors by trying to board a lift at the last moment when the doors are closing will always cause delay as the safety mechanisms cut in.

Above: The traditional escalators are still in evidence at the 1939-built St John's Wood, complete with the uplighters for illumination. The centre of the bank of three was constructed as a stairway, and remains as such. Presumably, an escalator could be installed here at some future date if it were deemed necessary. This photograph was taken on 30 August 1998. *John Glover*

Escalators too have problems; one of the best enforced 'rules' for passengers remains that of standing on the right. It has long been the situation that those who wish to walk up or down the escalator should be allowed to do so, but it is up to others to get out of the way and allow them to do it. This is something that has to be learnt by visitors to the capital, and can be very trying for Londoners at stations where there are large influxes of either domestic or overseas visitors. Conversely, one can often spot a Londoner in places such as Birmingham; many automatically stand on the right on shopping centre escalators, even though no such rules exist there. It may be said, also, that those who walk rather than just ride on the escalator increase its overall capacity.

There is, however, an alternative view. Long up escalators attract relatively few wishing to walk. As a result, overall usage of the escalators' capacity might actually decrease if a queue forms to gain access to the right-hand side. At stations such as Holborn, therefore, it can be productive to exhort passengers to stand on *both* sides in the morning peak, to help free the lower level circulating area.

The effectiveness of lifts and escalators does depend upon the number of each. The construction of additional shafts for either is not something to be undertaken lightly; thought has also to be given as to how new facilities will link in to the existing underground passageways. In practice, such work can only be undertaken in connection with major rebuilding. An example of this was Angel, Northern Line, where a growth in passenger numbers was making the narrow island platform (island in the

normal railway sense) overcrowded and potentially dangerous. The solution here was to build a new (northbound) platform in a new station tunnel, and fill in the trackbed on the northbound platform on the existing station. New escalators replaced lifts, and these consist of a short and a much longer rise. The upper set at 60m (197ft) is the longest anywhere on the Underground system. This set provides a vertical rise of 27.5m (90ft). Connected with this was the abandonment of the existing surface buildings and their replacement on a new site. The replacement of lifts by escalators always has this difficulty in that escalators are inclined at around 30° to the vertical, whereas lifts are strictly vertical movements. Something has to give, at either the top or the bottom end, or sometimes both.

Lifts should not, however, be disparaged too easily. They no longer need to be staffed, which resulted in a considerable cost in the earlier days. The strengths of lifts grow as the vertical distance to be covered increases. Speed, at least potentially, is in their favour. As has already been related, speeding up escalators tends to be self-defeating. The escalator shaft at Angel is impressive, but it can seem to take a long time to ascend or descend. The escalator versus lift debate, which for so long has been solidly behind the escalator, shows some signs of being reopened. One of the reasons is the greater depth at which new tube lines (CrossRail is included in this) have to be built in order to avoid building foundations, the pipes and cables of public utilities and also other tubes. Passengers arriving at Waterloo

Jubilee Line platforms need two escalators to reach the surface at street level and yet another to reach the main line station's platform level. (They may, of course, want the street.) With tentative plans being considered by Railtrack to extend the platforms on the main line station across the present concourse, and build a new circulating area at even higher level, yet another pair of escalators, up from the present concourse level and down again to the platforms, could be the result. A modern lift system might be far simpler and quicker.

Where escalators are unchallenged is in their ability to be used when stationary. Other than when they are under repair or being renewed and not safe for access, they can be used as stairs. No, they are not ideal, but a lift which isn't working is completely useless. Resort has to be made to the emergency stairs, typically in a modest circular shaft at many of the original tube stations. While adequate for their intended purpose, they are not suitable for normal volumes of passengers both entering and leaving the station. These now carry warning notices at the bottom informing anybody who chooses to use them of the number of steps up to the surface. Lift failure, if total, results in station closure until it can be corrected. Stations may also be closed by reason of escalator failure presumably because of the risk of being sued if somebody overexerts themselves and suffers a heart attack.

For the record, there were 100 lifts and 400 escalators installed on London Underground at the end of 1999. The number of lifts had declined gracefully over the years, but they have more recently

Above: A wide stairway leads from the Aldgate ticket office to a landing, from which stairs descend to the two island platforms. This is a building for crowds, and it was pictured on 18 April 1998. *John Glover*

been in favour again for the use of the disabled. The numbers of both lifts and escalators have swelled following the commissioning of the Jubilee Line extension and associated works. Approximately one third of all lifts and one quarter of all escalators are located at stations served by the extension. Canary Wharf station alone boasts three lifts and 11 escalators, and there is no physical connection between the Underground station with that of the same name served by the Docklands Light Railway other than via the street. Heron Quays DLR station is in fact nearer and more suitable for most interchange purposes.

Also worthy of mention is the long-extant travolator installation at Bank on the Waterloo & City Line which takes passengers from station platform level most of the way to the ticket hall at sub-surface level. More conventional machines were installed at Waterloo to link the circulating area at the bottom of the additional Northern Line tube escalators recently installed to the Jubilee Line. These are horizontal and similar to those at, for instance, Heathrow where they are used to link the Underground station with each of the three air terminals. The latter installations belong to BAA.

Travolators are in the same generic family as escalators, but most people using them walk rather than merely ride.

Ticket Halls
The continuous service associated with escalators can also deposit passengers into

an area where they are confronted with a line of Underground Ticketing System (UTS) gates. This poses an obvious hazard to movement, and is one reason why such barrier lines are staffed continuously. If any potentially dangerous situation begins to build up, all gates can be released.

The ticket office is intended nowadays to be no more than a place of last resort for ticket purchase, other than for tickets which are not available from the banks of ticket machines. These include period season tickets or Travelcards, and tickets purchased with credit or debit cards. Nevertheless, many passengers seem to use machines only if they have to and prefer to queue, occasionally for some considerable time.

It may be questioned as to whether the ticket machines are as easy to use as they might be, in terms of the choices offered, and it is always more difficult for visitors who are less familiar with the UK currency. A useful innovation observed elsewhere is the ability to request tickets for two adults and one child simultaneously, pay for them (and get change if necessary) in one transaction. To pay with a £5 note is much easier and quicker than to set the machine up to provide £1.60 tickets twice and £0.80 once. Sufficient ticket machines need to be provided to keep queues to a reasonable length, and this takes space. It is also desirable if the machines are kept clear of flows of those who already hold a ticket, to avoid each group obstructing the other.

New-generation ticket machines are, however, being introduced as part of the PRESTIGE project, under which all Underground stations have recently been gated. With ticket machines, too, it can be difficult to read the displays in bright natural light.

Below: One of the original lesser-used Yerkes stations on the Hampstead line is Mornington Crescent, still much in its original condition. After a funding hiatus, the elderly lifts were eventually replaced and the station reopened. Escalators were not seen as necessary here, which certainly simplifies the matching up of the ticket office area and the entrance/exit to the platforms, immediately below. The date is 24 August 1999. *John Glover*

Above: This admonition has the appearance of having been lifted from a 1950s road sign, but it is probably much older. The separation of passenger flows is helpful, if it can be achieved. This is the footbridge leading from the eastbound platform at North Ealing to the ticket office and street, on the afternoon of 20 March 2000. Shortly afterwards it was swamped by a tidal wave of schoolchildren arriving to catch their train home; the only sensible course of action was to 'keep out of the way'! *John Glover*

A cynic might suggest that ticketing system difficulties are less than adequately addressed as few railway managers ever have to make use of them!

Station Entrances

Above all, the station should be easily recognised by the passer-by for what it is. A prime position for the station entrance is at a road intersection, where two (or occasionally more) roads cross. Almost by definition, this is likely to be a busy place,

with plenty of Underground traffic potential. While originally surface entrances may have been provided, reconstructions in both the interwar period and more recently have resulted in ticket halls below ground level. Access can then be arranged from subway steps on each quadrant of the junction. Examples of this type of construction may be seen at Bank, Oxford Circus and Piccadilly Circus. Although it has been adopted widely, such arrangements do not allow passengers to be taken to or from the surface by lift, which is becoming more of a problem where the disabled are concerned.

At each of these three, a prime motivator was to link more than one line with a common interchange station. Bank qualifies as one of the most extensive, in that it links the Central, Northern and District lines, the Waterloo & City and the Docklands Light Railway. The distances covered underground by the unsuspecting passenger can be quite huge, since these railways were not built as close to each other as they might have been. It would be hard to suggest how the linking work to provide interchange could have been done better, but it remains less than ideal. In effect, it is the result of a variety of unconnected companies each pursuing their own objectives with little regard for those of others.

More satisfactory is Holborn, which the Piccadilly Line served from 1906, although the (earlier) Central London passed a few feet above. This was the subject of a major rebuilding in the 1930s, as a result of which British Museum station on the Central Line was closed and new platforms were opened at the combined interchange Holborn station on 25 September 1933. Here, a bank of four escalators descends from street level to a lower landing, from which passengers can continue by a second escalator to the Piccadilly Line area, or walk to the Central platforms. Nevertheless, congestion here has become a major problem, and entry to the station is frequently restricted. This is partly because of the inadequacy of the exit arrangements, and land has been purchased so these can be expanded.

Tottenham Court Road is another station which is seriously overcrowded on occasion, principally because of an inadequately sized ticket hall area and the inability of the escalators to take the volumes of passengers to lower levels fast enough. Here, passengers entering the station are encouraged to use the emergency stairs. A major rebuilding is proposed.

Such problems perhaps demonstrate that the railway as a whole operates as a system. Each part has to fulfil its allotted task, but the whole has to work in unison to prevent major mismatches of, for instance, capacity.

Car Parks

Without exception, station car parks owned by London Underground are well outside the central area. Those at Highgate, North Ealing or Wanstead are as near in as they come, though this does not, of course, include local authority or private car parks. There is a total of 65 car parks around the system, of which the biggest is at Epping. This has 599 spaces, as against an average of 175.

Car parks need to be managed, but they have considerable potential for attracting clients from a large surrounding area. The extent of this is always a potential problem on two fronts. First, if the result is that people from the Epping area drive to Woodford to park, that is a net loss of fares revenue to the Underground. Having said that, if others drive from the Harlow area and park at Epping, that is a total gain to Underground revenues and a loss to West Anglia Great Northern Railway. But, of course, the Underground can then argue that it is just as well that some Epping people *do* drive to Woodford, as this makes room at Epping for those from Harlow.

The second issue is the effect on road traffic volumes. If this results in more road use by motorists travelling some distance through congested areas, it is at best likely to receive unfriendly attention from the local authority. Maybe that doesn't matter too much, until one's success is such that one wants to extend the car park, for which some form of legal powers are likely to be necessary.

Fifty-eight station car parks have recently been equipped with a total of 587 CCTV cameras, as part of a drive to reduce vehicle crime. They are monitored by civilians employed by London Underground. The scheme was proposed jointly with British Transport Police.

A recent development is the appearance of cycle stands at a number of stations, to which bicycles can be chained at the owner's risk while travelling by tube. Cycle carriage on the Underground is very restricted, and not allowed at all on tube lines in tunnel sections.

Staffing

Almost all of London Underground's stations are staffed continuously during traffic hours (Roding Valley is one which is not). However, technical advances have made lower staffing levels possible; on trains, the elimination of guards was completed in early 2000, but the 'gatemen' of earlier times remind us that staffing matters were considerably more complex still before the introduction of power-operated doors. What of the station environment?

There are several groups of tasks to be undertaken:

- Providing passenger reassurance by a visible human presence.
- Sales of tickets.
- Monitoring UTS gates/ticket checking.
- Monitoring the operation of lifts and escalators.
- Control of passenger movements within the station generally, but particularly on platforms.
- Ensuring that standards of behaviour are

Above and right: One of the dot matrix indicators at Bermondsey station is on the pavement immediately outside the station entrance. When photographed, it was displaying, alternately, the two messages shown here. Perhaps Saturdays and Sundays scroll; the apparent omission of Saturday was not noticed at the time. The date of 15 March is, of course, for 2000.
John Glover

maintained.

- Providing passenger information and assistance.
- Responding to alarm signals (pumps, smoke detectors, etc).
- Opening and closing stations at the ends of the traffic day.

Similar commitments to station staffing at all times can be found in other major systems, such as Berlin, Madrid, New York and Paris. In medium-sized cities, though, staffing has sometimes been reduced to a partial presence or, in the case of Helsinki, Lille and Lyon, eliminated entirely.

Some of the tasks can be undertaken by roving staff or police officers; others can be monitored from a distance by the use of closed-circuit television installations. Systems which are built with this in mind are likely to be far more easily adapted to remote surveillance than old systems with many convoluted passageways and designs

which did not anticipate that staff might be less necessary at some time in the future. There is now much more equipment which will help to maintain a high level of security and functionality in both normal and emergency situations. The equipment which has contributed the most to reducing the need for a staff presence in stations is that for fire detection and protection (guaranteeing intervention), and telecommunications systems. These latter make it less necessary for staff to stay in one place in order to see how equipment is performing; consequently they can spend more time looking after customers.

While the Underground has maintained a comprehensive staff presence at stations, there must be at least some uncertainty that this should continue indefinitely at some of the outlying surface stations. Is a passenger usage (in a few cases) of less than 500 persons a day really enough to

support a full staff presence?

Plant Rooms

It may be necessary to provide for areas of the station to contain anything from telecommunications equipment to standby generators. Besides ensuring that ventilation for such equipment is adequate, care needs to be taken that any noise emitted is not excessive. Access needs to be maintained at all times.

A new feature is the provision of battery backup for the emergency lighting at all tunnel stations as part of the revised power supply arrangements. This replaces the duplication of electricity supplies from both London Underground and commercial electricity companies.

Travel Information

The Routes enquiry system is available for use by the Travel Information staff to telephone callers to 55 Broadway. Besides planning your route for you, this system includes details of each London Underground station. Thus a small station like West Finchley (Northern) is open from 05.10 to 01.10 Mondays to Saturdays and 07.15 to 00.30 on Sundays.

The ticket office is more restricted, being open only from 06.30 to 10.15 on Mondays to Fridays, with an evening shift from 17.00 to 20.00 on Fridays only. Saturday hours are 09.00-12.00, and 09.00-11.30 on Sundays.

Routes also records that there is a level entrance to the northbound platform ('level' here means down a slope with no steps in practice) but that use of the footbridge is needed to reach the southbound platform. This has 15+6 steps up and 6+15 down again; the second figures illustrate the change of direction at the intermediate landing. It is also recorded that there is a second entrance from Wentworth Avenue to the southbound platform, which is open 07.30 to 09.30 only. There are also lavatories for both sexes. The information is rounded off with the postal address and postcode.

Similar information is available for all others, but most stations are far more complex. They do, however, serve to answer detailed questions on the station and about disabled access, and exactly what is (or is not) available.

9

Performance and Infrastructure

Performance

To achieve adequate performance, whether from the fixed assets or the train service provided, is a commercial necessity. It is, after all, what the Underground's customers expect. Performance is something to be delivered, with safety.

What causes performance to slip? Glenda Jackson, then Transport Minister, provided an analysis of delays (*below*) to London Underground passenger services in 1997/8 to Harry Cohen MP:

Rolling stock problems accounted for a disgraceful 45% of the total. Add to these the 11% due to infrastructure, and the engineers seem to be responsible for 56% of all delays. Isn't it time that we found out how to build and maintain trains that work?

Operations scored better, but terminal management and driving techniques accounted for nearly 20% of the total. The public, in one way or another, were responsible for another 20% of the problems, of which 'anti-social behaviour' was by far the most important. Despite, or perhaps because of, constant harping on 'remembering to take one's personal baggage with one', delays caused by unattended luggage were few.

The total number of incidents causing passenger delays in 1997/8 were 32,356, or around 90 every day. Alternatively, this can be thought of as an incident occurring once every 1,800 train km. Such statistics do rely on definitions, plus the accuracy and rigour with which they are recorded. The severity or otherwise of the incidents will vary in terms of the amount of delay that they cause. Perhaps risk analysis techniques should be used to pinpoint the underlying problems. What sort of standards should LUL expect to be able to achieve?

Performance improvement, it should be acknowledged, is not necessarily easy. The Underground has recorded a consistent rise in passenger volumes with train km to match over recent years. More train miles

Cause due to engineering			
Rolling stock	14,543		
Signals, points	2,664	18,040	55.8%
Track	833		
Cause due to operations			
Terminal management	5,563	6,265	19.4%
Driving technique	702		
Cause due to public			
Antisocial behaviour	5,137		
Passenger ill or injured	610	6,579	20.3%
Unattended luggage	479		
Person on track	353		
Other	1,472		4.5%

Above: An insulated rail joint is seen in the foreground on a little-used crossover at the western end of Liverpool Street H&C platforms on 15 March 2000. Bull-head rail and wooden sleepers are in use. The rail nearest the camera has a wire welded to its top, to ensure that any train using it activates the track circuits through the increased pressure exerted on the rail. *John Glover*

mean more maintenance requirements, and more pressures on critical points in the infrastructure networks. Track congestion is a challenge to performance. To attempt to stifle traffic growth by real fare increases is not a practical proposition. The balance has to be a robust timetable and a planning regime which aims to get the maximum possible out of the resources available - but without incurring penalties for unreliability.

What are the main causes of infrastructure problems? If they are point failures, why do they happen? Is it a key component? Is it a few specific sets of points, or all of them? Does it reflect their usage? Are failures more prevalent at certain times of the year? Are there any recurring themes to be pursued? The identification of improvement opportunities and sharing of best practice can be very worth while. In no particular order, the following list suggests some

possible causes of infrastructure failure or problems, as well as points:

track circuits	power supply
broken rails	telecommunications
flooding	bridge bashes
hot weather	winter weather
leaf fall	trespass

Root cause analysis, taking into account the severity of the delays which ensue, can help by identifying the key causes. However, the importance of delays is not uniform. Railtrack classifies them under four headings, as follows. These show that incidents in a given period at 84 locations represent 24% of time lost in delays on Railtrack. For high-value locations, read busy and important ones. If the turnback siding on London Underground at West Hampstead (Jubilee) becomes inoperable, this is of little consequence, whereas a failure at Baker Street junction on the

Above: The old London Transport will take a long time to die. This sign is at Whitechapel, where it was pictured on 15 March 2000. It is clear and functional, with no chance of being misleading. Long may it remain. *John Glover*

Nuneaton showed that one set failed 22 times, 19 sets 5-10 times, five sets 10-20 times and 193 sets less than five times. Too many had high failure rates, and this was the beginning of a detailed investigation as to what was going wrong. Perhaps of some relevance to the Underground, one finding was that several sets of points had high usage but only very limited access for maintenance. It is also important that the maintenance undertaken is right for the job, whether in specification or execution. Parts must be correctly fitted, while human errors, unknown/intermittent causes, the need for renewal, and the technical standards applied all contribute. Analysis needs to concern itself with fact, not opinion. The causes of failure, such as interruptions to the power supply, may be less than obvious.

Maintenance needs to be optimised; quality is more important than quantity, while the risk of things going wrong needs also to be taken into account. Time-based maintenance regimes are well established, but modern signalling systems can record the number of times a set of points are operated. This gives the opportunity for maintenance on the basis of usage. Which is more relevant for the health of the asset concerned?

Other causes of delays more of a management nature might be:

- possession over-runs
- incident management
- contractor problems
- emergency services

The actions of emergency services and the occasional suicide are items which traditionally cannot be managed. Is this

Metropolitan, where it joins the Hammersmith & City Line, has major effects. More trains running mean more trains to be delayed by any incident and more minutes lost in total (see below).

It is not suggested that similar proportions are likely to apply to the Underground, but such classifications do enable meaningful management action to be taken. In Railtrack's case, analysis of points failures between Euston and

Location	No of locations	Time lost
high delay, high value	84	24%
low delay, low value	2,490	42%
low delay, high value	151	9%
high delay, low value	203	25%

Above: Cables across the line are one of the many pieces of infrastructure which have to be looked after; this, though, is for company use. The location is Colindale, looking towards Edgware on 21 March 2000, with a 1995 stock train disappearing into the distance.
John Glover

really so, or are there worthwhile steps which can be taken?

Possession over-runs on the Underground at night are a problem in themselves; up to a third of the total time available may be consumed in taking and giving them up. This is the time between when the last train has run, current is switched off and men and materials are in position to begin work, plus of course the reverse procedure in the early morning before commercial traffic is resumed. There must also be time allowed for the work to be passed as safe. On-track activity must be adequately protected, and nowhere is this more obvious than in tube running tunnels where there is no opportunity to stand clear of the running lines.

Engineers whose possessions do run over are not popular, since this delays the resumption of passenger services. Where management of the infrastructure is separated from that of the operation, this is likely to lead to penalties being extracted from the responsible party. Given that there are always unknowns in engineering maintenance work, managers are likely to over-estimate the time the job will take to make sure that they finish on time. In short, they build in a safety margin for themselves. More work may well be possible if all goes well, but there is a higher level of risk that it will not be completed on time. On the other hand, unit costs go down and the work is carried out that much more quickly. Who should be responsible for the risk element?

The choice is between the infrastructure company, its contractors, and the operating company, all of whom have some stake in

the outcome. Deciding the work which needs to be carried out is one thing; preparing an acceptable plan which ensures that it is all completed within any timescale which may be laid down is another. It must also not incur undue levels of cost, although staff productivity is constrained seriously by the shortness of the nightly shut-down.

The problem can be put as follows. A bridge needs replacing. The renewal can be undertaken in 52hr at a cost of £1 million. However, by committing more resources, it could be achieved in 26hr at a cost of £2 million. Here, there is a risk of both time and cost. What is the optimum solution?

It is suggested that any incentive framework needs to be aimed at helping the operation of the railway overall, and not encourage a 'somebody else's fault' culture.

Statistics

How well does the Underground perform? A range of quality service targets has been established and agreed with the Government as part of the Citizen's Charter programme. This is intended to gauge what the customers *think*, and is measured out of a maximum score of 100.

The results of the customer surveys show the perceived performance as being

Year ended 31 March 1999	Actual	Target
Safety and security, both assault and accident	81%	83%
Cleanliness of stations and trains	67%	69%
Station staff availability, helpfulness and appearance	68%	70%
Information quality on stations and trains	77%	75%
Train service quality of ride, level of crowding	75%	77%
Of the factual matters:		
Escalator service, % of planned hours operated	93%	91%
Lift service, % of planned hours operated	95%	94%
Train service, regularity of interval between trains		
Bakerloo	94.1%	94.8%
Central	93.7%	94.5%
Circle/Hammersmith & City	95.7%	96.0%
District	95.7%	96.2%
East London	98.0%	98.0%
Jubilee	97.8%	98.0%
Metropolitan	95.1%	96.5%
Northern	90.9%	94.4%
Piccadilly	91.0%	95.5%
Victoria	97.4%	97.7%
Underground network	94.3%	95.8%

Above: The Permanent Way depot at Lillie Bridge was unusually empty when this view was taken, although a Silverlink Metro train is passing on the West London line. This is one of the main engineering depots on the system. *John Glover*

rather worse than the targets, apart from the provision of information. Lifts and escalators though were better. On train service regularity, only the East London Line reached the target; overall, there was a 1½% shortfall across the network.

Operational Reliability

'Sweating the asset base' is nowadays accepted as a worthwhile way in which to reduce unit costs, but like other approaches, it can be overdone. In order to extract the most possible journeys out of the train fleet, train and train crew diagrams can get too complex for their own good. This leads to difficulties at one point being exported to another, and so on. Perhaps the asset base should merely be made to perspire gently.

More trains running means more of everything else, including delays, so the total actual delay is greater. This need not mean that overall performance has worsened in proportional terms, although it might.

High reliability comes from an approach where this takes precedence over novelty. Little to go right, little to go wrong takes one away from the cutting edge of modern technology, but the 1959 tube stock did go on working for a very long time. The A stock, from the same era, continues to perform reasonably reliably. The use of proven equipment of a limited and standardised range, in which updating means that any failures have been designed out, has much to commend it. Likewise, a maintenance regime in which redundancy is built into components so that they are just replaced rather than repaired saves much down time.

But this is not the way in which the British railway industry has progressed; even today, there are six different types of tube stock and three types of surface stock for a total of 12 Underground lines. Then there are the subdivisions based on whether or not cars have a driving cab, are motor cars or trailers, and so on. For a total fleet of less than 4,000 vehicles, this seems to be a lot of variation which would not be tolerated, for instance, in the motor industry. Then there are all the different types of lifts and escalators . . .

The reality is that there is a large variation in assets that nominally are doing similar jobs. They also have extremely long lives. The most productive approach would seem to be:

- Optimise what we have
- Find cost-effective new solutions
- Enhance maintenance effectiveness
- Prioritise resources to maximise impact
- Learn from experience.

Overall, there should be long-term cost-effective service delivery to passengers, and a commitment to innovation and development. To do this, the objectives of London Underground need to be a shared vision between the Mayor, the Opsco (operations company) and the Infracos, with as much long-term stability as can be achieved. If there is an appropriate framework of economic incentives, so much the better.

Bus Replacement

By definition, planning for random disturbances can only be an approximation. These can be anything from train door failure, through bomb alerts and signal failures, to flooding of the line or a railway underbridge being rendered unsafe to rail traffic as a result of being hit by a heavy goods vehicle.

Clearly, there is no single answer to such a catalogue of events, and they will all vary in their effects. Operationally, it is useful to localise the problem as far as possible; a bridge bash at Greenford can be met by diverting the main service to Ealing Broadway or terminating at North Acton. This leaves only the West Ruislip branch passengers to be catered for by some other means. The difficulty here is the time period involved; the bridge may be passed as fit for rail use within an hour or so, or it may be declared unsafe and in need of extensive repair. For that, rail services might need to be suspended for

Left: LT Buses' service 133 is a close parallel to part of the Northern Line, as can be seen from scrutiny of the destination and route blinds. When the Northern was closed for long-term engineering work south of Moorgate, the 133 was used as a major part of the replacement. As an ordinary scheduled service, this can be achieved by increasing the number of buses used, but keeping to the existing route. On 24 August 1999, VA 136 is seen in Princes Street as it nears Bank. *John Glover*

several days or longer. In the initial stages, the Line Controller will not know and some temporary arrangements are likely to be pursued. The simplest short-term expedient is for Underground tickets to be accepted for travel on scheduled local bus services, although passenger volumes can be a problem.

Where rail services have to be suspended for planned engineering works, it is usual for specific bus replacement services to be procured from an outside contractor. Such operations have to be defined with care, to make sure that the routes planned are feasible and that stopping points are available or can be provided at the Underground stations concerned. It is also most important not to contract double-deck buses if bridges only capable of accommodating single-deckers are on the intended route. This leads to the additional point that it is essential that everybody, including the bus drivers, knows exactly what is expected from them. Signage has to be good, and staff need to be on hand to guide passengers to and from the buses.

Left: While rail replacement services for the Underground need to stop near the station, this may be less practical than it appears. There is an escalator taking passengers from Highgate ticket office, which is in a cutting, up to the road a considerable distance above. This is the location for the bus stop, seen here on 24 August 1999. *John Glover*

Normally, travel is allowed only between the Underground stations, and not to or from any intermediate points.

One difficulty is in assessing the volume of bus replacement needed; a train containing 1,000 passengers will fill an awful lot of buses. As there is no such thing as pre-booking of travel on the Underground, the arrangements rely on the good knowledge of the staff as to what to expect. It is always possible to be wildly wrong!

In a loose sense, the Night Bus network replaces the Underground at night. By this means, most radial journeys in Greater London can be made. There is, however, no coordination at all between last trains and first night buses, be it in terms of timing, publicity or ticket inter-availability.

Track

Particularly in the central area, the track is very intensively used. There are few locations on Railtrack carrying the 20-25 million gross tonnes per annum of the District Line between Tower Hill and Gloucester Road, for example.

The track needs to be fit for purpose both in geometry and in its components to enable a reliable and punctual train service to be run. Thus the curvature, both horizontal and vertical, should not impose undue speed restrictions; if it does, adjustments need to be made if the business case supports action to alter it. Any speed restrictions that there are should not be imposed due to the condition of the track. Track components need to be robust enough to require minimum maintenance. Such characteristics also help the operators run a reliable train service, since they avoid or at least minimise closures for engineering works.

Ride quality needs to allow the vehicle to deliver the best that it is able; clearly the overall result depends also on the vehicle design and suspension system. Ride should also be reasonably quiet for the vehicle occupants, and not subject to noise such as from rail surface corrugations. These latter requirements are a reminder that vehicle and track together are part of a total system; the design and operation of each needs to reflect that interdependence.

The lengths of track in the various areas are:

- Surface   495km
- Sub-surface 90km
- Tube   241km
- Depots   253km

Underground track still relies heavily on bull-head rail, to the extent that less than 10% of the total consists of the now much more widely used flat-bottomed variety. The track support is similarly biased towards wooden rather than concrete sleepers. Half of all sleeper support is by ballast, but one quarter is ash. The remainder is concrete, as used in tube tunnels.

Civil Engineering Infrastructure

Similar requirements apply to structures, in that bridges and viaducts need to be of sufficient strength to support the trains using them without speed restrictions, and that civil assets generally should be maintained to avoid the need for unplanned closures. Embankments which fail, and there have been cases at Colindale (Northern) and Theydon Bois (Central), may cause speed restrictions and heavy maintenance in the short term, followed perhaps by total closure until the problem can be rectified. The Underground has 96km of embankments, 104km of cuttings and 854 lengths of retaining wall. This last mentioned is growing, as more earthworks reach the end of their life and require strengthening.

At Colindale speed restrictions were imposed, but a month later the track was being lifted three times a day until service was suspended. A 23m slip did occur and the northbound track dropped by 1.2m. Emergency works by sheet piling were

Above: The footbridge at Woodside Park station is a public right of way across the tracks, with the result that the station is effectively separated into two halves. There is access to and from both sides of the railway at platform level as well, but a ticket office only on the southbound (right-hand) side. This picture was taken on 21 March 2000. *John Glover*

carried out at a cost of £400,000. Investigations of this and other locations have found that most embankments consist of a clay fill core, mostly the spoil laid uncompacted from excavating nearby cuttings, and then overlaid with up to 2m of ash on the crest and to form side slopes. Nearly all such works are 70 years old or more; economy in the original construction has led to longer-term problems which are now coming to the fore.

Matters such as these point to sufficient asset knowledge to be able to plan ahead for work to be undertaken, but also to make sure that any necessary closures are used for as many different tasks in that area as possible.

Civil assets on London Underground include those listed below; those on the Jubilee Line extension are not included. As can be seen, even quite a modest system in terms of overall length, and much of which is underground, still has a large number of bridges with which to contend.

Underbridges	318
Overbridges	267
Cable and pipe bridges	189
Footbridges/subways	406
Viaducts	8km
Culverts	81

The typical tube tunnel is that with cast-iron lining rings. These were installed after the passage of the Greathead tunnelling shield which was used for their excavation. This method was universal in the Edwardian days when much of the tube network was constructed. Most survive today, albeit with some concrete replacements. Concrete has been the medium used in more recent times, notably for the Victoria Line in the late 1960s. Brick lining is of an altogether earlier vintage, and may be found on those parts of the Underground which originally were part of the main line railways, notably the East London Line.

The sections of 'covered way' are those occupied by the sub-surface lines, in which construction consisted of digging a trench for the railway and then, selectively, covering it over.

Cast-iron tunnels	206km
Concrete tunnels	33km
Brick-lined tunnels	25km
Covered way	103km

Finally, drainage of the track is all-important, and in tunnels this requires the use of 805 pumps to keep the trackbed dry. There are also large numbers of track drains and catch pits.

All such assets require regular inspection; bridges are inspected every four years, retaining walls every eight and deep tunnels every 12 years. Staff are also encouraged to report any problems which they encounter or about which they are concerned.

An unusual problem was detected in the cast-iron tunnel linings at Old Street, when it was found that the linings themselves were being attacked by naturally occurring sulphuric acid in the surrounding ground. Temporary strengthening of both tunnels was installed in 1991 pending a permanent solution. This was accompanied by regular monitoring for damage and movement. Later, a larger-diameter tunnel was excavated over the affected lengths and relined with stainless steel segments. It is not possible to undertake all such work in engineering hours, and some disruption to services is inevitable. The main problem with cast-iron rings is water ingress in some locations; this is of a different nature altogether.

A potentially troublesome problem has been London's rising water table. This has required an integrated strategy between London Underground, Thames Water and others to keep it from causing considerable damage. London Underground is presently pumping 30 million litres of water from the system every 24 hours, using a network of 1,050 pumps in 630 locations. This is equivalent to filling a municipal swimming pool every 20min.

Power

Power supplies must be of sufficient capacity to operate the scheduled services; this means not only that all the trains can move but that power shortages do not impose speed restrictions. Peak load power requirements need to be met.

Power supplies also need to be reliable. It should be remembered that traction is not the only power consumer: lifts, escalators, signalling, ventilation, pumps, lighting, ticket machines and numerous other services all use electrical power, and all need continuity of supply.

Power requirements tend to increase over time; lighting is always upgraded, never the reverse. Air-conditioning is not a business requirement, yet, but 20 years ago nobody even considered platform doors for the original Jubilee Line route from Baker Street to Charing Cross. In terms of power requirements, some services have a much greater need than others; it takes more power to accelerate a train with a thousand passengers on board than it does to switch on an extra light bulb, but the overall trend is always upwards. If performance improvements for train services are sought, this can have a substantial effect on the power bills, while the power supply infrastructure must be fit for purpose.

The majority of electricity to power the Underground is generated by the power stations at Lots Road, Chelsea and at Greenwich. Lots Road is in the process of being decommissioned and Greenwich will be used for emergency backup only. London Underground's power

Above: Underground trains are an unusual site at Iver, where a delivery from Alstom's Metro-Cammell factory at Washwood Heath was in progress on 6 November 1998. In the foreground is a Thames Trains local service to Slough. *John Glover*

requirements are to be purchased in future from commercial electricity suppliers. Under a 30-year PFI contract deal with Seeboard Powerlink, the latter will operate, maintain, finance and renew LUL's high voltage power distribution network. This includes substations as well as power distribution cables. At present, London Underground uses approximately 900 million units of electricity a year. Three-quarters of this is from its own two power stations, and a public supply meets the remainder.

Network Control

In any transport organisation as large as London Underground, a central point where the whole of the operation is drawn together and which performs network functions is extremely useful. London Underground's Network Control Centre was opened officially by the then Minister for Transport in London, Steven Norris, at the end of 1995.

The centre monitors all London Underground train operations. This includes the co-ordination of emergency incidents and the provision of passenger information. It is staffed continuously on a 24hr basis throughout the year.

As many activities as possible are devolved to the lines; Line Controllers have a job to do in keeping the operations running as near to timetable as possible and ensuring that train crew problems are sorted out. These are not tasks for an all-embracing organisation.

The Network Control Centre (NCC) forms the interface between the operational Line Business Units, the Underground's own emergency response organisation and the Press and Public Relations functions. The NCC also acts as the focal point during serious incidents,

Right: Station naming is very permanent if it is incorporated into the tiling as in this example at Tufnell Park, seen on 21 March 2000. The continuous name along the top of the wall is a feature of all tube stations. *John Glover*

liaising with senior managers and government departments, co-ordinating the use of resources and ensuring that timely and accurate information is available to all parties.

There will always be one manager and up to nine operators on duty, out of a total complement of 37 staff. The Duty Manager is responsible for the running of the Centre during a particular shift and supervises the operation of the Incident Desk, taking over direct control if necessary.

Incident Desk

The Incident Desk ensures that all incidents, major or minor, are effectively managed to their conclusion, with as little disruption to services as possible. This includes:

- The co-ordination of all serious incidents affecting Underground operation. Dispatch of both internal and external emergency services and subsequent liaison with them as the incident progresses.
- Maintaining comprehensive call-out details for out of hours contact with specialist managers.
- Disseminating information on severe weather conditions.
- Providing the point of contact for external sources of important information.
- Arranging catering for staff involved with serious incidents.

The Incident Desk maintains close contact with Line Controllers and Duty Operations Managers. All significant incidents are monitored and their effect on the network assessed by the NCC Duty

Manager. He decides when senior managers and directors need to be told of events. There is a communications system which enables all Line Controllers to be contacted simultaneously.

Information Desk

The Information Desk responds to situations which are usually notified first to the Incident Desk.

- This desk can make live broadcasts to all station ticket offices and most station control rooms, giving train and station information along with the estimated incident clearance time. The system is also used to communicate items of special interest to passengers, such as a football match being cancelled and also to staff, such as security vigilance messages.
- Message pagers are used to advise front-line staff of service information.
- Recorded messages are available to all staff through the internal telephone system. Updated hourly during off-peak times, half hourly during the peak and more frequently during incidents, this is handled by the Information Desk Operators and is a back-up for the live broadcast system.
- System information is also displayed on signs located at some main line station entrances. These give early warning to those arriving by main line trains of service problems.

- The NCC provides all real time information to the LT Travel Information Service and for transmission to TV Teletext systems as well as for the Underground's own radio studio, which broadcasts throughout London and the Home Counties in the morning peak.

The Information Desk processes all calls for the Emergency Response Unit. Requests for assistance can result from train derailments, passenger accidents, obstructions on the track and broken rails, as well as the more routine of deliveries signal equipment parts. The NCC maintains a computerised log of all vehicle and personnel movements within the Emergency Response Unit, ensuring that accurate information can be given at all times when attending an incident.

The Railway Display System provides an overview of services on a particular line and will alert NCC staff when service on a particular section of the network falls below a predetermined level. The NCC also has access to the British Transport Police CCTV pictures, enabling it to monitor passenger flows, overcrowding and the progress of incidents.

Fault Management

All communications faults reported to the NCC are passed on to the relevant contractor for attention. The NCC then chases progress until the fault is rectified. The reporting process covers automatic telephones, cables, police and Line Controllers' radios, and the NCC's own broadcasting equipment to ticket offices and station operations rooms.

The NCC monitors the state of the telephone network using computer systems which detect faults often before the end user is aware that a problem exists.

Alarm Monitoring

The NCC is actively involved in protecting London Underground's staff and assets from attack. A number of alarms are monitored to ensure a prompt response from British Transport Police. These include:

- Alarms for ticket offices.
- Ticket office safes.
- Staff alarms on single-staffed stations.
- Mobile Revenue Control staff alarms.
- Door access alarms.
- Fire alarms for telephone exchange.

Taxis

Taxis are provided for staff who are required to work extreme turns of duty. They provide a station-to-station service operating to specific schedules as requested. The provision of staff trains following the end of public services has now virtually ceased, the time being used more productively for longer engineering possessions.

Station Supervisors and Managers book taxis on behalf of their staff by telephoning the NCC. The booking of staff taxis is computerised, allowing connections to be made where a change of vehicle is necessary. The system also enables the operator in the NCC to check that the requests for taxis are bona fide and supported by personal identification details.

In addition, the Centre processes emergency staff taxi bookings in response to incidents at any time during the day or night.

UTS

Underground ticketing is based on self service machines, which issue a wide range of tickets and give change. Passengers are expected to use these, although a ticket window will be available for the issue of period tickets and the relatively few transactions not covered by the machines.

Tickets are checked by inserting them into a ticket gate at the originating station. Removal of the ticket by the passenger will open the gate. On exit from the system, the ticket is again inserted in a gate. A period ticket will be returned to the passenger and the gate will open on its removal. A single will usually be retained by the machine and the gate opens automatically. All this assumes, of course, that the ticket is valid.

A date capture and communications network covers all stations, to provide centralised accounting reports and current management information.

All faults on the Underground Ticketing System (UTS) equipment are processed by

Above: Subway Junction must have been a fearsome obstacle when built, as the Hammersmith trains had to cross the Great Western main line on the level. The mistake was soon rectified, and a C stock train heads away from the camera towards Paddington on 17 December 1998. There are no physical connections to Railtrack in this area at all. *John Glover*

Above: A miniature signal lever frame has survived to become part of the London Transport Museum collection. It was photographed on 6 February 2000. *John Glover*

NCC operators and passed on to contractors for attention. Corrective and preventive maintenance is also monitored. Station staff are assisted in resolving problems with the UTS equipment by talking through the correct procedures.

The NCC also controls the issue of UTS signing-on cards, protecting the system from unauthorised access.

Line Revenue Control staff are able to contact the NCC to verify an address through an Electoral Roll database, should a customer be travelling without a correct ticket. Penalty fares, it will be remembered, were introduced in 1994. As the Penalty Fares leaflet says, bluntly, 'You will be liable to a charge of £10 if you do not have with you, to show when required, the right ticket covering your entire journey.' It is not a fine, nor is it an accusation of trying to avoid payment. That is a criminal offence and may be dealt with by a prosecution made under the powers granted by the Regulation of

Railways Act, 1889. There are very few valid excuses for not having the correct ticket; being in a hurry and with no time to wait in the ticket office queue is not one of them. It will perhaps be of little surprise that dealing with violence associated with Penalty Fares enforcement is one of the main areas of activity of British Transport Police. The Force's Management Information & Communications Centre (MICC) is adjacent to the NCC in 55 Broadway.

As part of the implementation of the Penalty Fares Scheme, the NCC provides recorded information on stations with temporarily restricted ticket purchasing facilities and details of ticket acceptance for other transport organisations.

Signalling
Signalling is concerned with many train movements of a system used as intensively as the Underground. At Kennington signal cabin in the 1930s, the signalmen had to

control the working of over 1,600 trains a day, necessitating more than 13,100 lever movements, while there were only 32 levers in total. They were miniature levers, so this took care of the physical effort, but this is a good indication of the scale of the task.

The present signalling systems have already been described in Chapter 5. However, matters are moving as fast in signalling as in many other fields. A brief description of Transmission Based Signalling (TBS) follows.

Signalling that relies on fixed sections to separate trains has a certain inflexibility. Although the system and variations on it have served railways well over many years, it is relatively unsophisticated. Hence the development of transmission based signalling, which has the objective of keeping a safe distance between trains at all times.

TBS is a signalling system in which maintaining that distance is achieved by the continuous transmission of high resolution data from each train to a (static) control processor in the line control office. This is then converted into target points for the following trains. Data received from the control processor is then used by the trains to enforce the safety distance. It differs from conventional systems in two ways:

- train location is given by the processor on the train;
- the use of a bi-directional radio link, via the control processor, provides the information to the following train. The train processor continuously calculates the safety distance, based upon its own speed.

These systems are often described as 'moving block' although that is not strictly accurate. It is, however, much less rigid. As the position and speed of each train is known at all times, the TBS system ensures that each train has what might be termed a safety envelope around it and which moves with it. No other train may enter that envelope. The principle of no more than one train in one block at any one time remains; the difference is that the block itself is not defined as being between fixed points.

TBS enables trains to travel as close to each other as it is possible to do in safety, given the speed of the following train. When the speed of the leading train reduces, for a station stop for instance, the speed of the following train is also reduced to ensure that the safe braking distance is maintained. Thus, as trains progress along the line, their safety distance is not fixed by the expected highest train speed at a given point, nor by a traditional train detection system using track circuits. The system is continually adapted to the specific circumstances of time and place.

TBS benefits include:

- Virtually no trackside equipment.
- Little need to excess track for repairs/maintenance.
- Line capacity is not fixed at the signalling design stage.
- Bi-directional signalling can be achieved at little cost, though this, of course, depends upon the availability of crossovers between tracks to be exploited fully.
- In theory, recovery from delays should be faster, as trains can be 'closed up' like buses.

There are, of course, disadvantages also:

- The loss of the control processor would be catastrophic, with drivers reduced to driving manually, on sight.
- Radio coverage needs to be continuous and not liable to fade.
- Safety assurance must take into account the reliance on safety critical software systems.

Such systems have the potential of raising throughput to something in the order of 36tph.

10. Operational Safety

There is no such thing as absolute safety; it is a relative concept. All activities carry a degree of risk. It is certainly desirable to set standards, such as to ensure that risk is as low as reasonably practicable (ALARP), but it must be recognised that risk can never be eliminated completely.

Managers thus need to devise procedures for coping with the eventuality of major accidents. Recent events in both the aviation and railway industries show how traumatic these can be. In these modes, and also in shipping, casualties from a single incident can be high. Quite apart from the essential and priority tasks of coping with those killed or injured, and their relatives, there are many other matters to be considered. These include:

- Keeping other customers informed throughout and continuing to provide the best service possible for them at all times.

Below: Island platforms can be uncomfortably narrow, as in this one on the westbound platforms at Barons Court. The District is on the left, with a D stock train for Richmond; the Piccadilly tracks are in the centre. This is not to suggest that the platforms are unsafe, merely that their ability to absorb passengers in the event of major delays cannot be taken for granted. The continued use of a traditional clock which doesn't even carry the numbers 13 to 24 on its face is noticeable. The date is 20 March 2000. *John Glover*

Above: London Underground tried hard to close this footbridge just to the south of West Hampstead station platforms, but was defeated. It is now covered with close wire mesh, all over, giving a most uninviting appearance to pedestrian users. The justification, no doubt, is that it stops stolen televisions being thrown on the line. As a result, the carcasses litter the footbridge. A northbound A stock train for Uxbridge passes safely below. *John Glover*

- Facilities for and relationships with the media, maybe over a long period of time.
- Dealing with police, fire and other authorities.
- Communication issues between all those involved.
- Site access and clearing up the debris.
- The need to seek help from outside the operating companies, and the skills needed.
- Establishing the cause in an internal inquiry and consequential action.
- The stress suffered by transport industry managers and their families, and how this can be minimised.
- The effects on staff, many of whom are likely to know personally those directly involved.

- The need for individuals to be getting some sleep rather than be on duty continuously in the aftermath, and the delegation of authority.
- Disciplinary matters, legal involvement, liability and insurance issues and formal inquiries.
- Rebuilding customer relations and company morale.

Forewarned is forearmed, and the staging of dummy incidents can be a useful exercise for all concerned. Events, however, never repeat themselves precisely, and adaptation is always needed.

The list does not pretend to be exhaustive, but neither is it mode specific. Are there lessons to be learned by, for

Above: Turnback sidings are useful for terminating trains short, either as timetabled or in an attempt to restore normal working after some operational delays. However, it does take time to evict passengers who thought the train was going further. The turnback siding here is beyond the end of West Hampstead station on 20 March 2000; a Stanmore-bound Jubilee Line train is passing. Note that the points are set to neither road; any attempt by the train in the siding to leave will result in a derailment. *John Glover*

instance, railways from aviation, or railways from shipping?

Major accidents are an eventuality which each manager hopes will never happen, but statistics show that there will always be some unlucky ones.

Safety and Risk

How are risks estimated? The first step is to identify the individual hazards against which a guard is sought. Hazards they may be, but what is the frequency with which they are likely to happen and, if they do, how serious are the likely consequences? Provided reliable statistical data is available, these two approaches enable the risk to be estimated.

That risk needs to be appraised. Are further safety measures needed? If the

risks are high, the answer is yes. Those measures have to be devised, and then related to their effect on the hazard itself. The hope must be that they will, for instance, reduce the consequences, if not the frequency, of the event. An example from the motor industry is used as an illustration.

Such an argument would apply to attempts to reduce the level of injuries in car accidents. Some years ago the question arose of whether the compulsory fitting of seat belts would help. A risk estimate was established, the answer was positive, and the question of further measures considered. It was decided that seat belts were effective, but only if they were worn! Some compulsion was required, and it subsequently became law to wear them. Again, are further measures needed? If the answer is no, the situation is now satisfactory, and that is the end of the matter.

However, although car seat belts may reduce the *effects* of an accident, they do not address the *cause* and hence the *frequency* of the event happening. The cause might be too many drivers travelling too fast, with insufficient braking distance

Above right: Passengers in a 1992 stock train on the westbound platform at Bank, Central Line, on 13 April 1999. 'Mind the Gap' is a very necessary warning here. *John Glover*

Centre right: Help points are now found on Underground platforms; they have a multiple purpose, as indicated. This example is at Stratford and was photographed on 15 March 2000. *John Glover*

Below: Emergency stairs are part of the furniture, but don't tire yourself out using them! This set may be found at Elephant & Castle; they were photographed on 14 December 1999. *John Glover*

operational matters, and this has already been discussed in relation to station dwell times and door opening and closing routines. Questions to be answered perhaps are:

- Are any individuals placed at an intolerably high risk? If the answer is no:
- Take further action only if the benefits exceed costs.

The justifications for such an approach are twofold. That of equity means that no single group of people should be bearing a disproportionate part of the risk burden. Ensuring that further safety measures give benefits that are commensurate with their costs satisfies resource allocation efficiency. If they do not, the conclusion is that there are other ways of spending money, which will, pound for pound, provide greater benefits to society.

The question of Automatic Train Protection or other systems on National Railways is a relevant consideration here. Key parameters include what are considered to be acceptable chances of death, major injury or minor injury, and the valuations attached to each of them. These are not constant across all modes of transport, which is a problem in itself.

The argument so far has supported an approach based upon criteria, statistically verified wherever possible. However, there are severe difficulties. For instance, *this method does actually permit avoidable accidents to happen*. The accident could have been prevented, but the assessment said that it wasn't worth the expenditure, given the low chances of it happening and/or the small chance of serious injuries resulting. When avoidable events of a serious nature *do* happen, the train operator is going to be portrayed at best as incompetent and at worst as criminal, if identified deaths can be linked to specific decisions of that nature. Who accepts responsibility for the criteria used; is it the operator, the regulatory authorities, or ministers? There are also

Customer Information

DRIVERS
OF
Richmond TRAINS

Please make announcements about uneven PLATFORM AT Richmond when entering THE Richmond Station. Asking Passengers to take extra care

Above: Photographed at the end of the westbound platform at Turnham Green on 20 March 2000, this notice for drivers has nothing hi-tech about it. However, it does its job, which must be the main criterion. Now, why should such a notice be displayed here, when the train has to call at both Gunnersbury and Kew Gardens before reaching the Richmond terminus? Easy, these are all Railtrack stations, and London Underground has access rights only. *John Glover*

between them. Clearly, to attempt to deal with this, very different measures will need to be considered. On a railway, it is called signalling.

Should one do more to raise safety levels? There are always more measures to be taken, but an equally important consideration is do they offer good value for money? They may also impact on

Right: A standard two-aspect colour light signal, with a ground signal below, is to be found at the south end of Arnos Grove Piccadilly Line station. *John Glover*

the widespread effects of high-profile media coverage and the repercussions for the business itself. The King's Cross fire caused huge emotional costs as well as those of disruption and compensation, while there were also measurable declines in passenger usage of the station for the next couple of years.

Nobody pretends that there are any easy answers, and the principles apply to more than just train accidents. They are discussed here, briefly, so that readers can have some insight into the issues involved.

Safety Case

The Railway Safety Case Regulations, 1994, require London Underground to set out the way in which safety is managed within the company. The Safety Case has to be accepted by HMRI and by the owner of the infrastructure upon which the company operates. LU runs services over Railtrack between Queen's Park and Harrow & Wealdstone and also between Gunnersbury and Richmond. Also, South West Trains, Chiltern Railways and EWS run services over London Underground infrastructure.

Under the present restructuring of the Underground, it is intended that the three infrastructure companies (Infracos) will be sold to the private sector and the operations company (Opsco) retained in the public sector.

The principal contents of the London Underground Railway Safety Case are as follows:

• Endorsement by the appropriate manager
• Introduction, including the approach to safety
• Objective and scope
• Safety policy
• Appropriate risk assessment

- Safety objectives, goals, targets and measures
- Safety management
- Safety auditing
- Operational and technical standards
- Infrastructure control and maintenance
- Train operation
- Station operation
- Administration of safety cases
- Areas for development and improvement actions
- Conclusions

As an illustration of safety work, risk models have been developed to provide a quantitative assessment of major accident risks. Risks are measured in mean fatalities per year; the five highest in 1999 are listed in descending order, and some of the investment projects bearing on them are also listed *(opposite below)*.

The LUL Board's approach to safety improvement included the setting of safety objectives designed to focus the organisation's attention on key issues. These are underpinned by a range of key

Below: A train stop, at Mill Hill East, where its purpose is to prevent an arriving train overshooting the station and landing on the ballast. It was seen on 24 August 1999. *John Glover*

Below: London Underground is watching you, in this picture at West Hampstead on 20 March 2000. *John Glover*

Above: The platform-to-train interface has seen considerable problems, with passengers falling on the track between cars. Quite why this should happen is uncertain, but rolling stock is being fitted with flexible guards between vehicles to prevent this. A train of A stock was photographed at Farringdon on 15 March 2000. *John Glover*

- Platform/train interface   rolling stock management, CCTV, station works, interface management.
- Derailment   wheel/rail interface, track procedures, rolling stock refurbishment, signalling, structural repair, track improvement.
- Collision between trains   signalling, rolling stock refurbishment.
- Flooding   flood mitigation, pumps and drains.
- Station area accidents   congestion relief, escalator works, station refurbishment, lift installation.

performance indicators that include targets and numerical measures of progress. The annual Safety Plan complements the Safety Case. It sets out short and medium-term safety objectives and reviews recent performance.

At a time when Automatic Train Protection is an issue subject to wide public discussion, it is perhaps of interest to note the situation on London Underground. Here, there is a system which has full ATP on all passenger lines. If a train has to pass a signal at danger, as it may do under the rules to propel a disabled in front of it, its speed is restricted to 10-15mph.

Even so, London Underground still considers a collision between trains to be a key risk, where the systems of mitigation must be reviewed regularly for their effectiveness.

Above: The instruction is clear and simple; this example is on Chigwell station platform, where it was photographed on 12 February 1999. *John Glover*

Above: Escalators have an emergency stop button for use by the public if necessary, and there are warning notices to do with holding the handrail and not smoking. The illumination at a little below waist level is an innovation on these machines, part of the Canary Wharf flight, and photographed on 30 March 2000. *John Glover*

Conclusions

The sheer scale and present growth of London Underground's operations are remarkable tributes to those who had the foresight to build the first lines in the latter part of the 19th century, to those whose business acumen saw that it was developed in the 20th, and to those who have over the years seen that it has progressed as well as it has.

But old systems are not without their problems, and part of the lot of the pioneer is to make the mistakes from which others, to their relief, can learn. If we were starting again, we would no doubt do some things differently; it is perhaps unlikely that anything as constrained as the tube gauge lines would be considered. Starting again, though, is not on the

Below: Covent Garden station, once considered for closure, is now desperately overcrowded; in position it is ideally situated for the new market developments. Will its patronage continue to grow, and what works will become necessary as a result? This photograph was taken on 22 July 1999. *John Glover*

agenda. London must continue to make the best of what it has and to develop the system to meet new needs. This is the opportunity for major change.

The problems of the operator deserve attention and support; this is a highly complex area in which there is quite a thin dividing line between what is possible in terms of service provision, and what is not. Or, if it might be possible on a special occasion, it could not be sustained with the required degree of reliability.

Operational excellence cannot be separated from getting the very best out of the facilities and the assets which are already employed on the system. To meet what at present seems to be inexorable growth continuing for the foreseeable future, increased capacity will be essential. The principal alternatives, with all their attendant difficulties, are as follows:

- To increase the *frequency* of the train service operated.
- To increase the *capacity* of each train operated.
- To build new lines from scratch, in which one can choose the standards.

The first two have the benefit of being able to be put into operation relatively quickly and, compared with a new line, relatively cheaply. Put like that, they sound a good idea. However, readers will have seen the very real constraints on pursuing either of them too far, and the interaction between trains, their design, the service pattern, the signalling system and the stations to be taken into account. Perhaps most important of all, there is the question of how passengers can be persuaded to act so that trains spend as little time in stations as possible.

Finally, though, I would like to quote a now retired railway engineer from Maunsell's, Gerald Heath. 'Remember,' he once said to me, 'that railways and civil engineers have both been around for a long time. There aren't many things that we are unable to do. However, we do need to have studied the problem before we can say how much it will cost, what disruption it will cause, or how long it will take.' This is an example of the 'can do' culture, which has perhaps been less in evidence than it should have been in recent times.

Let tomorrow's operators take the same approach!

Right: Ticketing will take another step forward when the PRESTIGE scheme is commissioned. This picture shows the standard passenger-operated machines at Waterloo on 23 September 1997. *John Glover*

Below: The suburban station at Woodside Park looks much as it always has, with the addition of lighting, a roundel and a bus stop. Activity is noticeable by its absence. The date is 21 March 2000. Will these outposts of the network remain indefinitely as part of the Underground? *John Glover*

Left: The southbound East London Line platform at Canada Water on 20 March 2000 appears similar to those on the Jubilee Line, but there are no platform doors and the trains are of four-car length only. The whole is certainly spacious and built for growth; the trains of National Railways might yet be using this line again. *John Glover*

Appendices

Appendix I. Underground stations 500m apart or less

Line	Between	And	Distance (metres)
Piccadilly	Leicester Square	Covent Garden	250
Northern	Charing Cross	Embankment	270
District	Cannon Street	Mansion House	310
East London	Canada Water	Rotherhithe	320
District	Monument	Cannon Street	340
Bakerloo	Charing Cross	Embankment	370
Piccadilly	South Ealing	Northfields	380
Central	Chancery Lane	Holborn	400
Northern	Tottenham Court Road	Leicester Square	400
Jubilee	Waterloo	Southwark	440
Bakerloo	Edgware Road	Marylebone	450
Northern	Leicester Square	Charing Cross	460
Northern	Warren Street	Goodge Street	460
Piccadilly	Leicester Square	Piccadilly Circus	490
Bakerloo	Marylebone	Baker Street	500
Circle	Tower Hill	Aldgate	500

Appendix II. Adjacent Underground Stations more than 2,250m apart.

Line	Between	And	Distance (metres)
Metropolitan	Chalfont & Latimer	Chesham	6,190
Piccadilly	Heathrow Terminal 4	Heathrow Terminals 1, 2, 3	4,310
Metropolitan	Moor Park	Rickmansworth	3,490
Metropolitan	Chorleywood	Chalfont & Latimer	3,430
Metropolitan	Rickmansworth	Chorleywood	3,380
Central	Theydon Bois	Debden	3,340
Metropolitan	Chalfont & Latimer	Amersham	3,270
Victoria	Seven Sisters	Finsbury Park	3,150
Metropolitan	Moor Park	Croxley	2,940
Piccadilly	Hounslow West	Hatton Cross	2,910
Jubilee	Kingsbury	Wembley Park	2,850
Central	Stratford	Mile End	2,830
Central	Epping	Theydon Bois	2,540
Central	North Acton	Hanger Lane	2,490
Northern	High Barnet	Totteridge & Whetstone	2,460
Victoria	Highbury & Islington	King's Cross	2,450
Northern	Finchley Central	East Finchley	2,420
Piccadilly	Boston Manor	Osterley	2,420
Jubilee	Canada Water	Canary Wharf	2,410
Waterloo & City	Waterloo	Bank	2,370
District	Elm Park	Dagenham East	2,370
Central	Newbury Park	Gants Hill	2,360
Northern	Golders Green	Hampstead	2,340
Piccadilly	Turnpike Lane	Manor House	2,310
Central	Buckhurst Hill	Woodford	2,310
Jubilee	Wembley Park	Neasden	2,290
District	Barking	East Ham	2,290
Central	Roding Valley	Chigwell	2,280
Central	Northolt	South Ruislip	2,280
Central	Bethnal Green	Liverpool Street	2,270
East London	New Cross	Surrey Quays	2,270

This table ignores where some trains run nonstop over a section, as does the Metropolitan between Baker Street and Finchley Road.